reset

reset

FINDING A NEW COURSE AFTER DRIFTING APART

neil wilkie

The Relationship Paradigm

With grateful thanks to my wonderful wife,
Gwen Stirling Wilkie.

Mo Anam Cara. My soul mate.

About the author

Neil Wilkie was born in Scotland, but moved to the New Forest as a child. He spent many years in business, chartered accountancy, strategy consultancy, directorships and business ownership. A change of career in his fifties into psychotherapy led to him working with successful but unhappy people who were keen, like him, to discover their real purpose. This segued into relationship work, and after researching and experiencing conventional relationship counselling in the UK, he decided there was a need for a different approach, and set up Duo Coaching ten years ago.

Neil is no stranger to relationships and the multi-faceted experience they are. From falling in love aged twenty with a girl from the Caribbean but then marrying the girl next door, he escaped, bruised and battered after discovering her multiple infidelities, into the arms of a work colleague. Taking on her two children, and adopting two of their own, they had some good times, and some not-so-good times, and after twenty years, and three failed attempts at relationship counselling, they parted company.

It was at this time that Neil saw the need for more focused and supportive counselling, and has since worked with hundreds of couples, helping them move from a place of despair and unhappiness to one of closeness and harmony.

Neil is now married to Gwen, with whom both strengths and weaknesses are celebrated as they support each other in being the best they can be. Still living in the New Forest, he loves walking, cycling and sailing their boat, *Moon River*, south to the Med, a little bit at a time.

About this book

I wrote this book because I believe one of the greatest gifts anyone can have is a loving, fulfilling and sustainable relationship with another person. But how do we get to that when things have gone bad, or are lifeless, or there is no closeness anymore, and it seems the only choice is to split? I also wondered how to write a book that wasn't just another 'Read this book, do that, and it'll all be OK', because the shelves are weighed down with those.

It was then that I decided to write this book as a parable, to make it accessible to everyone, to help readers identify with Rachel and John's story as it unfolds, and be able to relate to the characters and their very different 'voices'. I wanted people to see that each of us has our own perspective, and experience and feel the same event so differently. I wanted readers to see themselves in the everyday scenarios that we have all been through and think, *Oh no, I say that*, or, *Yep, I do that*, and laugh, and cringe, and connect with our couple's battle to get back to each other.

Having experienced this first-hand, I know how hard it is to talk to each other about the really important things that are causing difficulties and pain, and be trapped in a cycle of blame and misery. Helping couples find each other again, and even fall in love again, is the greatest joy. But it's not just the couple who benefit. The impact on their children, friends, families and work relationships is incalculable.

The work Maria and I do with couples is immensely rewarding, and there have been many tears of happiness at witnessing the actual moment when a couple reconnect and fall in love again. Sadly there are only so many people we can see, and I wanted to find a way of helping people all around the world to create and sustain great relationships. Writing this book, the first in a series, is a way of reaching those people.

I hope you enjoy reading the book and get some value from it. I hope it helps you in your relationship, and you are able to talk openly about it with your partner. I hope you can really listen to each other as you explore what could be even better in your relationship, because you both deserve to have that.

Thank you for reading.

Acknowledgements

There are so many people I need to thank for this book.

The first is my wonderful wife Gwen, without whom this book would never have happened. Your encouragement and support got me from dreaming to doing.

Second is my daughter Michelle, who came into my life at the age of fifteen months and has shown me the power of love. Believe you can, and you will.

My parents, for my start in life, and providing some stability through tempestuous times.

My sisters, for coping with my differences and being there for me.

Maria, who I work with in Duo Coaching, for your deep insights and different perspectives. You are a joy to work with in creating great outcomes for our couples.

My friend Gill, you have supported me through climbing the mountains of the world and the mountains of life.

Max, my last-ever best man, for your support, wisdom and great conversations.

Adam, possibly the world's best coach. Your ability to pinpoint what I had been avoiding is scary.

My members and colleagues at Vistage for allowing me into your lives to help you to develop yourselves, your relationships and your businesses.

My clients, for letting me into the inner recesses of their lives and trusting me to help them on their journeys.

All the ladies with whom I had loving relationships. I was never trained to have a good relationship, and have learned by trial and error – with lots of errors! Thank you for the learning, and I hope your journeys have been positive.

Tian, for converting my voice into text. You made the process so much easier.

James, Stefan and the amazing team at SpiffingCovers for your creativity, professionalism, help, support and guidance in bringing these words into physical reality.

My incredible editor, Kimberley, for converting my random words into something that makes sense and is readable. Your encouragement has been amazing.

And lastly to this incredible world that we live in, full of joy and challenges. May we create loving and sustainable relationships within it.

A glass is never empty; it is always full of possibilities.

Praise for *Reset*

*"Neil has produced that rarest of books. One that shares great ideas about how to improve our relationships without falling into clichéd stereotypes or preaching. He uses the example of a couple whose relationship has fallen on difficult times. We have all been there. **It is a brilliant book that educates, inspires and entertains.**"*

– David Thomas, Sunday Times #1 bestselling author

*"This is a wonderful book and a stunning idea. The stories, from different perspectives, are just so compelling. I felt such compassion for John and Rachel. **This is a book for every couple who has become jaded with life, love and passion.**"*

– Nikki Owen, bestselling author and international speaker on charisma

*"From the first paragraph I was hooked. The story has you feeling you are right there, watching and seeing the remarkable changes happening to John and Rachel. **Whether you are in a great, indifferent or failing relationship, you will find wisdom here to get you starry-eyed and madly in love with each other.**"*

– Frank Furness, international bestselling author and motivational speaker

*"Wow! This book is a true game-changer. We are often blinded by our own perception of what reality actually is, and struggle to see and empathise with the other person. **This book allows you to put yourself 'in their shoes'.**"*

– Adam Harris, author and coach

"What a refreshingly easy read about a couple's journey from intimacy, to separateness, and back to love. In writing Reset, Neil has managed to capture the loneliness and desperation that many of us can relate to when love and intimacy leave a relationship. Having experienced Neil's process with my husband, I cannot recommend this important book highly enough to those many couples who know life should be more enriching."

– Lindsey Kleinlercher, award-winning retailer

"There are many 'How to…' books on relationship issues. These can be useful and informative, but somewhat dry. Neil Wilkie takes a different approach in Reset that we really like: the inside story of a wife and husband with a real-life issue. Many couples will enjoy reading Reset and will learn how to improve their own relationship at the same time."

– Penny Tompkins and James Lawley, authors of Metaphors in Mind: Transformation through Symbolic Modelling (and married for 27 years!)

"Every now and again a book comes along which really does add something new to our understanding of relationships. This highly readable book draws on Neil Wilkie's experience of working with hundreds of couples. Thankfully, it is not telling us to 'do' anything, but rather to reflect on our own relationships. I spent half the time reading, and the other half asking myself challenging questions."

- Jeff Grout, business speaker, consultant and coach

THE RELATIONSHIP PARADIGM

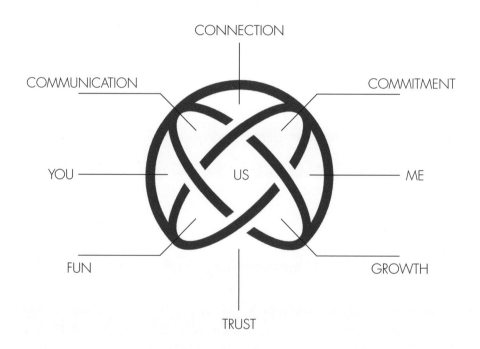

CONNECTION

COMMUNICATION

COMMITMENT

YOU

US

ME

FUN

GROWTH

TRUST

CONTENTS

CONTENTS continued

Don't treat others as you would like to be treated, treat them how they want to be treated.

– Neil Wilkie

Prologue 1 : John

At thirty-nine, and sixteen stone with a bit of a beer gut, I know I ought to spend a bit more time on myself, getting fitter. I play rugby at the weekends; but I guess the beers with the guys afterwards don't help too much with that! Sundays I sometimes do a bit of gardening, if the weather's OK, but then fall asleep after lunch, which doesn't go down too well with Rachel, my wife. (Ditto the beers and sometimes coming home a bit pissed on Saturday.)

I commute into central London every day, leaving early and getting home late. I'm a partner in a law firm, and specialise in corporate finance. I admit I'm a bit of a snob. I like bespoke suits and my 5-series BMW and opera, loud. Rachel loves rock music, which I hate. And sailing, which I also hate.

We have three children, James, Jennifer and Rowena, who I don't see that much, which I feel sad about if I'm honest. We also have a dog – well, Rachel's dog – who I don't like and didn't want because he covers the house and my suits in his bloody fur.

I don't expect perfection, but the state of the house sometimes... What does Rachel do all day? I know she has the kids to take care of, and dinner to cook, but honestly... And as for our sex life... Seems I'm just here to fill our bank account and the house with nice stuff and get little in return.

Recently, I've been wondering about me and Rachel. I'm not that bad-looking, tall with (thinning, I admit) dark hair and eyes, and a broken nose (from playing rugby at university) which gives my face a bit of character. I don't expect things to be how they were when we met, but she barely even looks at me these days, let alone smiles. Think it might be time to get that Porsche...

Prologue 2: Rachel

I'm finding it hard to see any fulfilment in my life. I'm thirty-eight, feel frumpy and a bit overweight, and have no career – I had to abandon my dreams of being something great in the marketing world when the children were born – and go to the gym mainly to try and get Pierre, the hot personal trainer, to notice me, and to gossip with the women I've met there.

What happened to the fun-loving me, dancing and singing at rock concerts, with all her plans of sailing and travelling? Now I'm just stuck in this big house, married to John, who is rarely here, with three kids – who I love, by the way, but who make loads of mess and stay glued to their iPhones. (Well, the older two do.)

When I look in the mirror, I see my same curly brown hair, my really blue eyes, but where am I? Where have I gone?

I get the feeling John wants a Stepford Wife, with a big, shiny white smile and a sparkling house to go with his BMW and his ladder-climbing career. But in truth I'm so tired. I don't want to make an effort. And I don't want to make love – if you can call John's beery-breathed climbing on top of me on Sunday mornings that.

I don't know what I want. I just know I don't want this...

Prologue 3: The Children

James

I guess I don't remember much about the first few years of my life. Mum and Dad and I used to play a lot together, though, and do silly things. I remember being upset when Jenny arrived. I felt a bit out of place. She cried a lot and it wasn't much fun having a new grumpy baby sister. The fun seemed to disappear then, and Mum and Dad had lots of arguments.

I first went to nursery school when I was four, which was great because it got me away from Jenny. When I was eight I went to the prep school, which was OK except that I had to go with Jenny, which was really embarrassing. Rowena was born when I was about four. She is really sweet, but I feel I have to protect her from her sister too much.

Four years ago, we moved here. It's much bigger, but I lost all my friends, which was not OK.

I'm supposed to be going to boarding school in September. Dad wants me to go there because he did. I'm a bit scared about it, as I don't know what the other children will be like and I don't want to share a room with a stranger.

Dad loves rugby and takes me to his club every Saturday afternoon. That was fun until recently, because when I turned thirteen it became contact rugby, which I find really scary. I have told him I don't want to go any more, but he won't listen.

I find it a bit stressy at home, and I prefer to go up to my room and play on my PlayStation. I only really see Dad at weekends as he gets back from work late. Mum seems a bit sad and grumpy most of the time, and always seems to be telling me off.

Jennifer

I hate my life. I'm always being told off and everyone around me is so miserable. James is horrible to me, and Rowena is really irritating; she is also Mum's big favourite. I don't like being at home. Mum's got no time for me and Dad is never there. I can't wait until I am old enough to go to boarding school and then I can escape.

Rowena

I love Mum; she is so kind to me. James is really good, too, because he saves me from the evil Jennifer. I wish I had a magic wand and could make Mum happy. She seems really sad most of the time and I don't know why.

Dad is OK, but he is away at work a lot and not really interested in girly things. Woody is brilliant. I love cuddling him.

I have fun at my school and have some really nice friends.

Chapter 1: Friday - John

It was the beginning of another normal day in the lives of what, from the outside, must look like a happy and successful couple.

Radio 4's Today programme woke me, quietly, at 6.00am. Rachel was gently snoring with her back to me, feet away on the other side of our super-king-sized bed. I rubbed my face and wearily stumbled out of bed. Another day at work beckoned.

Fighting my way through the bottles of shampoo and bodywash lying on the floor, I went for a shower, and then dressed in the half-dark, because Rachel always shouted at me if I turned the light on. My wardrobe was in chaos so I grabbed the best combination of shirt and tie I could find.

I groaned in despair at the mess in the kitchen; the sink full of dirty dishes and the expensive granite worktop covered in half-read women's magazines and chargers for electronic devices. I switched on the coffee machine and fed it with a pod. There wasn't a clean mug anywhere to be found, so I had to fish a dirty one out of the dishwasher and rinse it out. I noticed my iPhone battery was almost flat: one of the bloody children had obviously pinched my charger. I opened the fridge to get some milk, but there was none. Shit! No coffee, and no milk to have with my cereal either. Today was a big day at work. I was due to complete on an acquisition and then have a departmental partner's meeting. What a great start. I gave up on coffee and breakfast and I called goodbye at the foot of the stairs, but there was no response from anyone; so in a louder voice I said, 'I'm going to work, for too many hours!' and slammed the door behind me.

The drive to the station only took ten minutes, but it took another ten to find a parking space. I saw the train coming in and had to run to make it, feeling hot and sweaty and bad-tempered by the time I sat down. My mood was not improved by the fact I was next to a very large girl, dressed as a Goth, listening to very loud and very tinny death metal music. The next forty-five minutes were annoying, and there was not enough room to get any work done. I arrived at Waterloo Station and inserted myself into the horde heading to the Waterloo & City.

Today was the scheduled completion meeting for a deal I had been working on for the last six months: a management buy-in of a medium-sized fashion retailer. It was valued at £100m, and was the biggest I had been in charge of. The deal was on a contingent basis, which meant that if it wasn't put away my firm would earn nothing. If, as scheduled, it happened today, then the firm would get fees in excess of £500k, and I would get some much-needed kudos that might get me closer to the frustratingly distant target of becoming a full equity partner, which meant my earnings would more than treble.

The journey to Bank passed in a bit of a haze, with me dreaming about the Porsche Carrera I would be able to buy and which colour to go for: metallic dark blue with a magnolia leather interior, or slate-grey with black? In the short walk to the offices in Moorgate, the dream continued with thoughts of maybe a motorbike too; a big Harley of some sorts; a real midlife crisis bike. I had been working hard for this firm for seventeen years, and I'd had so little recognition. Similarly, from Rachel and the kids. I was the provider who kept them in the style they had become accustomed to, but got very little appreciation. Soon it would be time to treat myself; it was only what I deserved.

I walked into the marble foyer and took the lift to the tenth floor. The firm had five floors in the building, and this was my floor, with the corporate finance teams. The equity partners had the enclosed offices around the edge, with a view of the city. I was in the open plan space with my team of ten juniors and support staff. The firm had about 700 staff in total, with fifty equity partners. The number of partners had not grown in the last ten years, as billings were fairly static. In truth, I was waiting for dead men's shoes to get promoted. Maybe today was the day in which all my hard work would pay dividends.

I got to my desk. There in neat piles were all the files of jobs I was currently working on. I logged in on my desktop and checked my schedule for the day. I had the morning free, a pre-meeting with my management buy-in, Clive, at 12.00 to run through the final points of the deal, and then a full-blown completion meeting starting at 2.00pm with the vendor, their solicitors, Rathmore Curtis from Leeds, and Belvoir Corporate Finance, who were masterminding the deal, the private equity house, NWV, who were funding a large part of the deal, and the bank, Barclays, who were putting in a substantial amount of debt to the deal. It was going to be a big meeting, in separate rooms. It should only take two hours, but if there were last-minute changes, it could run into the small hours. I felt the adrenaline start to flow.

My secretary Kim stuck her head around the side of my cubicle and asked if there was anything I needed. Kim was young, bubbly and blonde, and I admit I had often wondered what would happen if I took the first step and suggested a drink or dinner. With the way things were with Rachel, I was really tempted; but it would be a step from which there might not be any turning back.

I said I needed three things: a charger for my iPhone, somewhere where I would be uninterrupted for a couple of hours to check through all the papers, and for Kim to make sure the meeting rooms were all set up for the afternoon. Kim smiled and said, 'Sure thing.' A few minutes later she came back with a charger in one hand, which she handed to me, and winked. As I took it from her I felt a surge of energy as our hands touched, and I looked her in the eyes and smiled. Kim smiled back, told me the meeting rooms were set up, and that I could lock myself away in one of the rooms for the morning. She had already made me a coffee, and said it was waiting there for me, with some fresh fruit and granola bars.

I thanked her, plugged in my phone, assembled all my files and headed to the room. I took a grateful sip of my coffee, bit into a bar and started to work through the files. It was a fairly straightforward deal, with the price based on a multiple of six times historic earnings. All 200+ shops were in prime positions on fairly standard leases, and my property team had checked through all these and found nothing unusual. The Sales and Purchase Agreement and warranties were standard, and there was little room for negotiation on these. My experience was that if a deal went sour there was little point in bringing an action against the vendor, as the cost and time involved in doing this was prohibitive.

I decided I would spend the next two hours looking at the numbers again, as these were critical to the valuation of the business. PFR, a reputable firm of chartered accountants, had worked on the due diligence, looking over the final accounts for the year ended March 2017 and certifying that the numbers stood up. The profitability at £17m showed substantial growth over previous years as a result of an aggressive store-opening strategy. It was now 15th January 2018, and the management accounts for the first nine months had just been received.

I took another sip of coffee and opened the management accounts file. I was no accountant, but something looked wrong: the numbers were smaller than I expected, there were no comparatives, and the format was different to the previous year. I dug out the 2017 numbers and tried to make some sense out of them, scribbling down some numbers on a pad to find comparatives from 2017. After many minutes of head-scratching and searching, I felt a cold shiver down my spine: my ballpark numbers showed that profitability had plummeted by over 60% since last year.

Picking up the phone I called Luke, the partner at PFR.

Luke answered the phone, sounding cheerful. 'Hi, John. Are we all ready for closing the deal at 2.00pm?' I explained what I had found, and was shocked by Luke's carefree reply: 'I'm sure it'll all be fine. We were only asked to look at the year-end numbers and, anyway, we're all on contingent fees, so if the deal does not complete, we'll all be out of pocket.'

Next, I called Michael, the partner at Belvoir Corporate Finance, and was shocked to get a similar response.

The phone then rang, and it was Kim telling me that Clive, the purchaser, was in reception early. I hurried back to my desk and picked up my now-charged iPhone. I saw there was a voicemail from Rachel and listened to it. She sounded angry and wanted to know where I had put her car keys. Bloody cheek!

I went down to reception to collect Clive, who greeted me with a wide smile. 'Today is the big day!' Clive said.

We went up to the meeting room, and I asked him if he had seen the latest numbers. Clive said he had, that they didn't make much sense to him, but he was sure they were alright; after all, he had all these expensive advisors to look after him!

I took a deep breath and told Clive I had just been looking at the latest numbers, and that profitability looked like it was way down, with Christmas sales having been well below expectations.

Clive looked puzzled. 'What does this mean?' he asked.

I spelt it out, very simply: on the basis of these numbers, the business was worth £40m not £100m.

Clive went pale. 'Shit! Why did no one tell me about this? What do I do?'

My advice was that they needed to explore the numbers more and, if they were true, to go in with a lower offer. Clive said he didn't think their vendor would accept a penny less. I said, if that was the case, Clive would be paying two-and-a-half times what the business was worth, and cash flow would cause huge problems. Clive asked about the view of PFR and Belvoir. I told him I had spoken to them, and that they hadn't looked at their latest numbers. I kept quiet about the fact that their focus was getting their deal done so they could get their fees and leave Clive holding the problem. I asked Clive what he wanted to do. Clive said he trusted me to do what was best.

The time rolled by very quickly and, at 2.00pm, we met with the team backing their deal: Luke from PFR, Michael from Belvoir, Nick and Simon, the partners from NWV, and Tony from Barclays. They were all looking excited at finally getting the deal done. I sat them all down and explained the problem. Their faces fell, and they all turned to Luke.

'Why didn't you spot this before?' Nick asked angrily.

Luke simply said, 'This wasn't in our terms of reference, and we had to rely on the information from the vendor.'

I felt my phone vibrate and pulled it out of my pocket. It was a text from Rachel: *John, I need some more money. The decorator has to be paid now. Can you transfer £1,000 to my account?* If I could have thrown the phone at the wall I would have. I felt like phoning her back and screaming at her. Did she have any idea what went on in my day?

I stood up, faced the room and said, 'I can't advise my client to sign on the deal if these numbers are true. We have to get the vendor to explain, and maybe this is an opportunity to get a significant price reduction. With your agreement, I will go and speak to the lawyers representing the other side and see what they say. Is that OK, Clive?'

I was surprised at how calm and determined I was now feeling. I could have gone along with the crowd, done the deal and let Clive suffer the consequences; but that would have been against my professional ethics. Even if all those juicy fees disappeared out of the window, I would be able to hold my head up high if I challenged this.

I turned and left. The vendor and his lawyer, Julian of Rathmore Curtis, were waiting expectantly in the next room. I had come across Julian a few times before, in previous deals, and thought him a nasty, aggressive little man. I asked Julian if I could have a few words and showed him to an adjacent room. I explained the situation to him, and he looked surprised and said, 'Well, the deal has been agreed and the price is the price. It's a good business and your client has got a great deal; there isn't any room for negotiation.'

I felt my anger rising, but said there was no way, on the basis of the latest numbers, that the business was worth £100m, and that Julian should speak to his client and find out why they had only just come clean on a dramatic downturn in profitability. I gave Julian an hour to come up with a solution, and turned on my heel before he could respond.

I walked back into his meeting room and was greeted by a sea of expectant faces. I explained what had happened, and the responses were muttered curses. Clive looked like a rabbit caught in the headlights.

The next hour passed very slowly. Finally, there was a knock on the door, and Julian came in. He looked around the room and said, 'My client says the downturn in profitability is just a short-term blip due to a change in buying focus, and that this will correct itself in the spring collection. He is adamant there is no reduction in price, not even a penny.'

Feeling surprisingly brave, I said, 'And what are the current stock levels?'

'I don't know; I will go and find out,' Julian replied.

Ten minutes later Julian returned and said, 'About £20m, at cost.'

I dug through my files. 'That's about six months' worth of stock...about four times what it should be?'

'Well, that's a great opportunity for your client,' Julian answered.

But I looked at him and said, 'Unless your client significantly reduces the price, then we don't have a deal.'

'That is not going to happen,' Julian responded, and left the room.

The room went quiet. I didn't know much about fashion retailing, but I did know that if the stores and warehouses were stuffed full of unsaleable stock that would crucify cash flow and brand image.

Clive turned to me and said, 'What should I do?'

'If you knew what you know now, would you still pay £100m for the business?' I replied.

Clive gulped and said, 'No way.'

I felt my phone vibrate again. Again it was Rachel. I excused myself and answered the call.

Rachel launched straight into me about a hundred things. My response was very short and abusive, and I ended the call.

I went back into a very quiet room and said, 'If the vendor is not prepared to reduce his price, do any of you want to proceed on the current terms? I certainly could not advise my client to do so.'

Nick, Simon and Tony all said there was no way the deal could go ahead on the current numbers, and that they were really disappointed that Belvoir and PFR had not picked up this problem much earlier. They said they were really grateful I had done my research, and had made a tough call, and left the room.

Clive, his shoulders slumped, shook my hand, thanked me and left too.

I turned to Michael and Luke and expressed my disappointment that I was the one who had discovered the problem when it should really have been picked up by them. They muttered something and they, too, left.

I headed for the senior partner's office. Peter was busy on his computer when I walked in, but asked if the deal was completed yet. I slumped in the chair and told the whole story, expecting to be given a really hard time. But Peter looked me in the eyes and said, 'On the one hand, we have lost £500k in fees; on the other, you have saved our client from a catastrophic outcome and boosted our credibility with the bank and PE companies. Which do you think is most important?'

I said, 'I think I did the right thing.' And then added, 'But I've been here for seventeen years, and haven't got to the level that I think I deserve.'

'Yes, you did the right thing,' Peter replied, 'and I'm impressed that you did. As far as your future with the firm is concerned, I've been worried for some time that you've just been going through the motions. You arrive in the morning looking disengaged and unhappy, and during the day your mind seems to be on other things. Maybe if you had been on top of your game you would have spotted the problems sooner? What is really wrong? Are things OK at home?'

Before I could think about my reply, I simply said, 'Yes, fine.'

Peter looked closely at me. 'Maybe a couple of weeks off would help you get over what has just happened?'

'Maybe...' I pondered. 'Thank you.' I left the office.

On the walk back to the Tube station I bumped into an old friend who worked at another law firm, and we went for a quick drink at a pub in Moorgate. One pint turned into several as we shared our complaints about work, love and life, and several hours later I found myself back at East Horsley realising I was not in a fit state to drive home. I phoned Rachel and got no answer, so I started the long walk in the drizzle.

All the lights were off in the house. I stumbled up the stairs, walked into the bedroom and heard Rachel snoring. She mumbled something at me. I said something back and I fell onto the bed and passed out.

Chapter 2: Friday - Rachel

I heard the alarm go and John get out of bed. I groaned quietly. If only he would be quieter in the morning. I had an hour before I needed to get up for the children and I needed my sleep. Last night, and the previous few nights, I had woken up several times with bad dreams and a feeling of dread about the future. I felt alone, unhappy and drifting apart from John.

My alarm went off at 7.00am and I went to wake the kids. James came first. I opened his door. His bedside light was on, and his phone and iPad were on the pillow next to him. I spoke quietly, but when I got no response I shook his shoulder. He grumbled something and sat up. I opened his curtains and went in to Jennifer's room. I sighed at the state of it, and got told to fuck off and had a shoe thrown at me when I tried to wake her. I retreated, but slammed the door. Finally, Rowena, in her lovely tidy room with pictures of fairies everywhere and a bed full of teddy bears. She turned over and smiled at me, and reached her arms out for a hug.

In the kitchen, I made a space on the worktop and laid out three bowls, spoons, plates and knives. I poured three glasses of orange juice, got the boxes of cereal, yoghurt and milk out, and sat and waited.

I reflected on my life, where I had hoped it would be, with an satisfying career, a loving husband and days full of excitement and challenge. I reminisced about life fourteen years ago, when the world seemed to be at our feet, and me and John working as a team, having fun and enjoying a simple life together. Now it felt as if the weight of the world was on my shoulders. I wandered through to our large living-room, newly decorated with expensive wallpaper and curtains. I looked at the huge flat screen TV that John liked to watch Sky Sports on, the pile of remote controls, many of them with the battery covers missing, and then wandered over to the bookshelves and absent-mindedly picked out a few of the self-help books I had bought, full of hope that my life would magically change if I read them. There must be so many answers within the covers. If only I could find the time and focus to read more of them.

On the mantelpiece over the fireplace I caught sight of the picture of me and John at the register office on our wedding day. It was a casual photo taken by a friend, but it captured the joy in that moment; the love that shone in our eyes just after we had been legally pronounced man and wife. I then studied the large framed picture which had been taken by a studio photographer last year. I had signed up to a free sitting, and had dragged the three children and John along. The 'free' sitting turned into a subtle but high-pressure sales pitch to pay over £2,000 for this large framed picture, which I hated. We were all sat there looking as if we would rather be somewhere else; no sign of connection between any of us other than Woody looking up adoringly at me and Rowena stroking him. What sort of family were we, really?

Remembering Woody, I rushed to the utility room where he was patiently waiting in his basket. He was the one member of the family who gave me unconditional love; the only one I could talk to about anything. I stroked him, bent down and kissed the tip of his nose and said, 'Good boy.' I then opened the back door and, beginning to show his age, he slowly got up and wandered into the garden to relieve himself. I remembered the discussions and arguments that had gone on for years about getting a dog. John was adamant they were too messy and too much of a tie. Realising I would never win the argument, I started looking for a puppy anyway, and, one day, eight years ago, brought an eight-week-old Woody home. The children were excited, particularly Rowena; but

John was incandescent with anger. He insisted that I took the puppy back, but I refused, and over the next few weeks his anger faded. But he never connected with Woody and frequently complained about the smell and the mess.

I went to the fridge and got out some of the raw chicken mince that Woody loved and mixed it with some fruit and vegetable pulp. I put it down outside, and he bounded over and ate it in seconds.

There was still no sign of the children, and we had only twenty minutes before we needed to leave. I shouted up the stairs, and got no response. James was still in bed, so I pulled the duvet off him. Jennifer was in bed, too, looking at something on her iPhone. I grabbed her phone from her, yanked open the curtains, and told her we only had twenty minutes. Rowena was dressed and standing at her mirror brushing her hair. I smiled at her and said, 'Breakfast is ready, sweetheart.'

I quickly dressed and went back to the kitchen. I was on a diet that I hoped would help me feel better, detox, and lose some weight. I looked at the shelves of cookery books to the right of the Aga, and was shocked to realise how many of them were diet and juicing books rather than good, old-fashioned cookery books. I had insisted the kitchen in this house should be replaced with an expensive limed oak one, with an Aga, and a whole range of expensive appliances. The irony was that I rarely cooked, preferring to buy ready meals from Waitrose. It was really a show kitchen, installed to try and impress the friends I rarely saw.

Rowena ran down the stairs and poured herself a bowl of muesli. A few minutes later, Jennifer came down, scowled at me and said, 'Where's my phone?'

'I will give it to you when you've had breakfast,' I replied, to which Jennifer gave a barely muffled curse and said she wasn't hungry.

James then appeared, glued to his iPhone, and said he wanted some toast. I put some bread in the toaster for him and, remembering myself, put some kale, spinach, carrot, apple and spirulina into my

Nutri-Bullet and turned it on. I poured it into a glass, tasted it, and pulled a face. It was disgusting, but I supposed it was good for me. I drank it quickly, hoping to bypass my taste buds. It didn't work. The toast popped and I handed it to James, who spread it thickly with Nutella. I then put some Cocoa Pops and milk into a bowl for Jennifer, who scowled but started to eat them.

Noticing the nasty taste was still in my mouth, I hurried the children up, grabbed my gym bag, called Woody, and shepherded everybody out of the door. Where were my car keys? I searched in my pockets, and then my bag. Getting desperate, I phoned John – perhaps he'd seen them this morning? – but got no response. I felt angry and left a blunt message. He is never there when I need him. I tipped the contents of my bag onto the drive – they had to be in there! – but no keys. Then I remembered I'd worn a different coat yesterday, and there they were. Relieved, I unlocked the car and locked the house. Woody got into the boot, Rowena in the front, and James and Jennifer bickered in the back.

First stop was prep school, which was about ten minutes' drive away. As we got closer, the number of yummy mummies driving their 4x4s increased. I hated this school: the cost of it, the pretentious parents, and the over privileged children who went there. The teachers were OK, but it was a very cloistered, unreal environment – very different from the state schools I had gone to. John had insisted his children should have the best possible education, as he had; and when his parents offered to pay for the first two children it was difficult to refuse. Their generosity ran out when Rowena was born. I drew up at the entrance and, as Jennifer and James, still in thrall to their iPhones got out, said, 'See you at five.'

The next few minutes on the way to Rowena's junior school passed quickly, with her talking excitedly about her role in the upcoming school play and her dreams of becoming an actress. I parked a few minutes from the school and walked her to the gate, holding her hand and smiling at some of the other mothers. I got a hug from her, and said I would see her at three thirty.

Now time for a walk with Woody. I drove to the nearby woods, and headed south on one of my favourite walks. Woody walked beside me, occasionally picking up the scent of rabbits and running after them with enthusiasm, but there was little chance of him catching any. The walk gave me the opportunity to clear my head and think about what I needed to change in my life.

I thought about John; how much I had loved him when we first met, and the excitement of setting up house, getting married, and having James. Tears came into my eyes as I realised I didn't feel love for him anymore; in fact, I didn't even think I liked him anymore. So many of the things he did annoyed me. It was as if I was now looking at him in the distance through a telescope, and thinking I wanted to be somewhere very different. I reflected on the fact we very rarely talked – unless to complain about each other. And when I tried to talk to him about important stuff, like the children and their education, it would often end in an argument that culminated in me crying and John slamming the door and going into a huff for several days.

I also remembered our early days of love-making; full of fun, laughter and naive experiments that brought us closer together and really connected us. That had all disappeared into the mists of time, and now, on Sunday mornings at 8.00am (well, most of them), I dreaded the moment when John, with his stubbly face and breath stinking of beer, would roll over and grasp me from behind, and I would feel his erection pressing against me. He would then roll me onto my back and, with no real attempt at foreplay, climb on top of me and well, that was just how it was. I had long ago given up trying to change this routine, and had been unable to talk to him about my needs; so, with the aid of a bit of vaginal lubricant and some pretend groans, I instead put on a good act in the hope that he would come quickly and get off me. My own pleasure was reserved for the week, when the house was empty, and I could liberate the faithful battery-powered friend I had named Pierre, after my personal trainer at the gym.

I thought about the children, too, who I felt a great sense of love for. But, if I was honest, I was finding it hard to like James or Jennifer. I hoped as they grew through the difficult teenage years that would change, but it seemed like a long and thankless journey.

I also thought about my friends, none of whom I felt really close to. They were fun people to occasionally share a coffee with, but their focus seemed to be on spending their husband's money on flashy new cars, new kitchens, clothes and makeup, whilst bitching about them. I had joined them at their own game, I knew that, but did not have anyone else I could be totally honest with.

Five years ago, in despair about our relationship, I had dragged a very reluctant John along to see a marriage counsellor. When we left the first session, after fifty minutes, he had refused to go back and face another session of being told it was all his fault.

I had wondered what it would be like to have a temporary escape from my unsatisfactory marriage; I had even wondered whether the real Pierre, my personal trainer, would be up for a quick affair – something that would make me feel a real sensual woman again? I had allowed my fingers to linger on his hand a bit too long a few times, but he had not taken the hint. Then, last week, I had seen Claire, one of my so-called friends, saying farewell to Pierre at the gym with a long, lingering kiss, and knew he was otherwise occupied.

I had tried talking to my mother about how I felt, but after I found out about my father's ten-year affair, thirteen years ago, I knew that the shutters were up and talking to her about emotions was not possible. I now felt like there was no escape; I just had to make the best of it. My older brother Victor and me had never been very close, and after he left his wife two years ago for his young assistant I felt angry with him, and we don't really talk any more. My younger sister Paula was a bit of an emotional hoover and was of little use. I decided I needed to find my own answers, and had become an avid collector of self-help books, delivered freshly

THE RELATIONSHIP PARADIGM

wrapped by Amazon…but the answers were remaining tantalisingly out of reach, and I felt insecure looking at their happy faces and hearing about how they'd got it all worked out.

My phone bleeped: it was Andy, the decorator, texting me reminding me that his bill was outstanding, and could he come around this afternoon and pick up the cash. I quickly sent a text to John, as I did not have enough money in my account.

I then sat down on a bench overlooking the fields and started to think about the future I wanted. I realised that after fifteen years and three children I couldn't just walk away and start a whole new life; what I needed to do was try and talk to John and see what could be rescued from what we had. A plan started to form. This evening I would play the dutiful wife and cook him a lovely meal, with candles, and try and rekindle some romance. I would try and make love, on my terms, for the first time in many years, and maybe get him to agree to going away somewhere, just the two of us, where we could talk and try and connect again. It was Friday, so hopefully he could leave work behind and we could start our weekend in a good way.

With the plan came some glimmerings of hope, and I headed back to the car with Woody, stopping off at Waitrose. John had fairly traditional tastes in food and I decided that something simple, fairly light and easy to cook, would be best. I chose smoked salmon as a starter, fillet steak with a green salad for the main course, and fresh fruit salad for dessert. A glass or two of a dry Prosecco to start with, followed by a nice Malbec from the Mendoza region of Argentina for the main course, would go down well. I also decided I needed to get the kids to bed early and would cook for them, from scratch, a shepherd's pie, with a choice of Ben and Jerry's ice creams for after. My trolley full, I paid for the shopping and headed home.

I was feeling excited and more in control than I had felt for a long time; and when I got back home I sat down in front of my computer and looked at places John and I could go on holiday. It needed to be somewhere warm, a place where we could relax. After a few minutes of browsing, an ad popped up for a place called Sandals that was offering sixty percent off. I was intrigued – and a bit scared that Google seemed to be reading my mind – but clicked on the ad and read more. It looked perfect, with a range of locations across the Caribbean and many daytime activities. I clicked some more, and saw a baffling choice of rooms and prices, but good availability. I homed in on one of their resorts in Grenada and printed off some pages.

I then picked up the phone to my mother, and explained I was planning a surprise two-week holiday with John and would they be able to come and look after the children. My mother was initially reluctant, but then I heard my father's voice booming in the background: 'Tell Rachel of course we will; we would love to have the opportunity to come and sort them out!'

So, the plan was falling into place. All I needed was to get John to agree. I phoned him to ask him about Andy's cash, and to tell him about the dinner plans, and was really hurt by his abusive response. *Maybe he's having a tough day at work*, I thought, unusually charitably.

The afternoon passed quickly. I picked up a bouncy Rowena from school and took her for a walk with Woody, listening to her chattering animatedly. We then went to join the queue of 4x4s outside the prep school and picked up a quiet James and a scowling Jennifer. I told them dinner would be on the table at six thirty, and that I wanted them in bed by eight as I was going to have dinner alone with their dad at eight thirty. They all gave me a funny look, and headed up to their rooms.

I felt a bit hurt by John's response on the phone, but felt determined to stick to my plan. I got out the ingredients for the shepherd's pie and set to. The hour passed quickly, and I felt a sense of pride and motherhood at the smells coming out of the Aga. At the dot of six thirty, Rowena appeared and started setting the table. I called up to James and Jennifer and, as usual, there was no response. I thought, *This is crazy*, but reached for my phone to send them both a text. A few minutes later they magically appeared.

Jennifer headed for the fridge, opened it and said, 'Where's the Coke?'

'There isn't any. Have some water or fruit juice.'

I was amazed when Jennifer said, 'OK.'

All four of us sat round the kitchen table, with the children eating enthusiastically and Woody waiting expectantly. Rather than asking them the usual 'And how was your day?' I just sat and waited, drinking my glass of water. I was delighted when James started talking about his day and the fun they had in chemistry. I was even more delighted when Jennifer smiled and laughed about her afternoon cross-country running. Rowena also joined in and, just for a moment, we looked and sounded like a family. *Who are these children?* I thought, looking at their faces, seeing how much they were growing and changing.

The ice cream then came out and the three of them got through a big part of several tubs of different flavours, talking, joking and laughing. When the children, without being asked, cleared the table and loaded the dishwasher, I came over all faint with surprise. They then said, 'Thank you!' and all ran upstairs, chatting and laughing.

I fed Woody, made the green salad and fruit salad, set the table for me and John, poured a glass of Prosecco, put on some not-too-bad black underwear and one of my favourite simple, black dresses. I looked at myself in the mirror and thought, Shame about the hair, but the rest is pretty much OK. I then went down to the living-room and put my feet up, listening to one of my favourite singers, Gordon Haskell, and waiting with anticipation for John to arrive. On Fridays he was normally home by no later than eight.

The music finished and I looked at the clock. It was eight thirty. Where was he? I picked up my phone and called him: no answer. I rang again, and no answer again. I then sent him a text saying, *Dinner is ready. Are you OK*? and waited and waited for the answer that did not come.

Upset and disappointed, I put on some mindless TV, and phoned his mobile again, and his work number, but got no response. Two hours later, feeling rejected, and slightly worried, I went upstairs. The children were all asleep, so I turned off their lights and went into the bedroom. I took off the black dress, hung it back in the wardrobe. The black undies too, which I shoved back in the untidy drawer. I ran a bath. As I sank into the warm bubbles I felt pretty sad that John had not appeared, and remembered the many evenings where he had come home late after meeting a drinking buddy. I also thought about how different the kids had been that night, maybe because I had properly cooked for them, and spent time with them, rather than firing off a list of questions.

Just as I was falling asleep I heard the front door open and John stumble up the stairs. As he walked into the bedroom, I realised I had a choice of responses, ranging from an angry 'Where the hell have you been?' to a calm 'Are you OK?' I decided to try the novelty of the calm and concerned question.

John replied, 'I'm sorry, it was an awful day at work and I bumped into Will on the way home. I'm afraid I might be a bit pissed,' and fell onto the bed.

I got up, undressed him and covered him with the duvet. I then got back into bed and eventually managed to get to sleep, despite his loud snoring next to me.

The next morning, I woke up early and looked at him, lying on his back, still snoring, and thought, I once loved this man...I wonder if I can love him again?

I went downstairs, made a strong black coffee for John, a peppermint tea for myself, and let Woody out into the garden. Walking back into the bedroom, I opened the curtains and sat down on the bed next to John. I touched him on the shoulder, and he woke up with a start. A frightened look passed over his face. I handed him the coffee and he smiled, and looked relieved.

After taking a sip he said simply, 'I'm sorry.'

'I feel sad and lonely, John. It seems...it seems we have drifted apart, and I want us...I'd really like us to go away for a couple of weeks, and see if we can fix this.'

John sat upright in bed. 'Are you leaving me?' he asked.

I hadn't mentioned leaving? Where had that come from? 'No,' I said, calmly, 'but we can't go on like this anymore.'

'So, what are you suggesting?'

'All I'm suggesting is that you take two weeks off work and we go somewhere where we can relax and talk to each other.'

'Why can't we do that here?'

'I've tried many times and you just won't listen to me.'

'But what about the children?'

'My parents are going to come and take care of them.'

'When...and where do you want to go, and how? –'

'I've found somewhere in the Caribbean which looks great; they have availability in two weeks' time and the price will be about £5,000, all inclusive.'

'We can't afford that!' John said.

'We can't afford not to.'

'Do we have to?'

'Yes, I insist.'

'Can I think about it?'

I replied with surprising determination: 'Yes. You have until 12.00 noon today.'

John looked at me in amazement. 'Shit... What has got into you?'

'I've just realised how important it is to get this right, and it's not something I'm going to allow to fade away or just walk away from. The ball is in your court.'

I got dressed, quickly made another revolting juice for myself, and took Woody out for a walk.

When I got back an hour later I walked into the kitchen – and was amazed to see the children all sitting round the kitchen table talking and laughing. John was at the Aga making waffles. He smiled at me and said, 'I've just been telling the kids I've decided that the two of us are going away for a thirteenth wedding anniversary celebration to the Caribbean. And Jennifer has shown me how to make waffles with the waffle iron on this stove!'

I sat down for breakfast, upset that my initiative had been hijacked. After breakfast had finished and we'd cleared away I said to John, 'What just happened?'

John said, 'I thought about what you said, and I acknowledge you need a break. My boss even said that I need one, so I've checked my diary and we can go two weeks' today. So shall I book something?'

Chapter 3: Off to the Caribbean - John

I was really surprised by Rachel's response on Saturday morning. All that talk about being sad and lonely. I know I had been late back and should have called her, but didn't she understand what a huge disappointment Friday had been for me? She still hasn't asked me what happened at work, and that makes me feel she just isn't interested. Sometimes my only release is to go out for a drink with a friend. Rachel and I can't really talk about man stuff.

The idea of two weeks somewhere relaxing was a good one. I don't like being forced into something, though, and only agreed because Peter had suggested I take some time off. I normally like to be in control of big decisions, but this time I thought I should give Rachel her head and let her decide and book it.

I don't know why Rachel gets so stressed. She has an easy life doing her own thing, with no pressure. She doesn't have to get up early every day and go and sit in an office in London dealing with some real arseholes. I do wish she would keep her side of the bargain and keep the place tidy; it's not much to ask.

Hopefully a holiday will get her sorted out. It will be so much nicer to be greeted by a smiling wife, happy kids and a tidy house every evening.

The kids have seemed a bit happier recently. It's a shame I haven't had much time with them in the past. I've had to work really hard to get things sorted out so I can take two weeks off, and haven't had much time to talk to Rachel either. When we have talked she's been excited about where we are going and shown me lots of pictures. It looks great, but bloody expensive. I hope it's worth it. Hopefully Rachel will get in the mood for some more sex; once a week is really not enough for someone as young as me.

Things started to get a bit more tense a couple of days ago. I left Rachel to sort out the packing. She went and bought me some new t-shirts and shorts. I'm not sure what was wrong with the ones I had – although they must have shrunk a bit, as they were a bit tight; probably because she stuffs everything into the tumble drier – but I just smiled and said thank you. I feel a bit like I've been walking on eggshells and having to be deliberately nice. It was almost better when we were shouting at each other. At least then I knew where I stood.

Then on Friday her parents arrived. David is a bit weak and henpecked, and Kathleen just takes over. Still, the kids like them, and they will keep them safe while we are away. When I got back on Friday night they were all playing Monopoly like a happy family. Shame they hadn't waited for me.

Saturday, we left early to get to Gatwick by 8.00am. Rachel had done all the packing and all I had to do was carry the bags to the taxi. It felt really strange not being in control; almost as if I had been emasculated. Rachel had checked in online with Virgin. I wasn't very impressed when I got on the plane, though, as I had a middle seat and we were behind a crying baby. She should really have got us a free upgrade.

Chapter 4: Off to the Caribbean - Rachel

I was really shocked with myself for being so assertive. I was also very surprised that John seemed to accept it without going off in a big huff. I still don't know what happened to him on Friday; maybe I should have asked but I've been really busy.

So, we have two weeks in the Caribbean, and free of interruptions. I just hope we are able to talk about us, as I can't go on as we are. I'm not sure how to get John to open up, though. He really doesn't like expressing his emotions and just doesn't seem to understand how desperately unhappy I am. If it wasn't for the children I don't think I would stick around anymore.

The last two weeks have gone very quickly, and life seemed to go back to almost normal after me telling him I was unhappy, which disappointed me. John seems to believe that all this is about me, and a holiday will put it all right. He's been very busy at work and our conversations are short and superficial.

The children have been a bit better and I tried to make time just to be there and listen to them. I was surprised at how a little thing like cooking them a special meal on that Friday could make such a big difference to them. There were more smiles and less shouting.

John agreed to let me choose and book the holiday, which must have been the first time ever. I just hope he likes it, otherwise I will never hear the end of it. I did try and sort out his clothing, and had to spend a lot of time persuading him that ten-year-old shorts and t-shirts that strained to cover his beer gut were not acceptable. I bought him some new things, which will make him look a bit more presentable.

The Friday before we were due to fly out, my parents arrived. Mum was laden down with containers of food she had prepared in advance, and went around the kitchen moving things about and tutting. Dad just smiled at me, raised his eyebrows and said, 'Just bite your tongue, dear.' The kids were pleased to see them and after a dinner, that Mum cooked, we got the Monopoly board out and started playing. Shame John didn't make it in time.

Saturday, arrived and feeling excited and very nervous I got into the taxi. This is the first time John and I have been away for more than a weekend in the last fifteen years, so it feels a bit strange. He even allowed me to take care of the passports and boarding cards, which, for a control freak, was a bit weird. When we got on the plane it didn't take him long to start complaining, though, so I put my headphones on and spent the next eleven hours listening to my music.

Chapter 5: Rachel Meets Olivia

Well, Sandals in Grenada, our first time in the Caribbean and, I'm hoping, the beginning of a new and much better chapter in our lives. We were hit with a wall of heat as we stepped out of the plane, bright sunshine and strange but lovely smells. The hotel had arranged to pick us up with a few other couples and we were driven the short distance to the hotel, which looked as good as in the photographs.

We were shown to our room, which was huge, and had a big balcony overlooking the pools and, on the balcony, was a large double bathtub. It felt great. I persuaded John to leave the unpacking and get his swimming shorts on and come for a swim. There were several pools and the one closest to us was huge, with a large swim-up cocktail bar, so after a few lengths, I ordered a cocktail. John was already there, holding a large glass of beer.

I felt the worries and tension begin to fade away and was thinking that the next two weeks could be really good. John looked at me, raised his glass and smiled. We had a few more drinks as the sun slowly set and, slightly unsteadily, then made our way to our room. I suggested to John we should go and find somewhere to eat, so we quickly unpacked, got dressed and headed down to the restaurants. We were feeling tired and in need of some quick food, so we chose the buffet restaurant, which had a large spread of hot and cold food to choose from. We sat at a table for two, with our plates full, and I realised that this was the first time in at least two years that we had sat down, just the two of us, for a meal together. There was an uncomfortable silence, however, and it felt like we were two strangers with not much in common. What could we talk about?

I smiled and touched John's arm. He smiled back and said, 'Thank you. This is lovely. You made a good choice.'

I felt a little glow spreading up from my stomach and said, 'Yes, it does look lovely.'

We talked a bit about the children, wondering what they were up to, and then finished our meal and headed back to our room. I asked John if he fancied a bath. He went outside and had a look and said, 'What would happen if someone walked past?' and got into the shower.

I waited until he had finished and then had a shower myself and got into bed. John was sitting in a chair looking at his emails. 'Are you coming to bed?' I asked.

'Yes sure,' he said. 'Just a minute,' and focused back on his screen.

A wave of tiredness swept over me, and the next thing I was aware of was the sun streaming in through the curtains and the sounds of birds singing. I turned around and touched John, who was fast asleep, on the shoulder. He woke up, grunted and looked at me. 'What's wrong?' he asked.

'Nothing,' I said. 'It looks like a beautiful day.'

John laid his right arm over me and started tweaking my nipple.

'Ouch,' I said quietly, as it hurt, and moved his hand to lower on my breast.

'Oh,' he said, sounding upset. He got up and went to the toilet. I then heard the shower running.

Not a good start to the day, I thought, with a tense feeling in my stomach. But I walked into the shower, just as John was getting out, and said, 'Let's have breakfast and go and explore.'

We both got dressed and I sensed a growing tension between us. Breakfast was delicious, but conversation was almost non-existent. John looked glum and I started to worry that he would be like this for the next two weeks. I scanned the room and was struck by the number of couples who were there, smiling and talking animatedly to each other. I felt we really stood out as being misfits. I was particularly taken by one couple sitting at the table next to us. They were speaking in English and must have been in their fifties. She was blonde, pretty and well preserved, and he was a bit older, balding and quite fit-looking. What really struck me was the loving way they looked at each other, their gentle touches, and how much in tune they seemed. I tried to listen surreptitiously to their conversation, which seemed to flow effortlessly, and noticed how the gentle silences seem to add to the conversation. I thought they must be on their honeymoon and reflected on our three days in Paris and how different that was.

I started to wish we could be like that again. What would it take to turn the clock back and fall in love, like we had been? A feeling of sadness washed over me as I realised I could not turn the clock back, and maybe we were forever trapped in a relationship that could only ever be just about OK.

After breakfast we borrowed a map of the area and walked around, taking in the beaches, water sports, diving, different pools and range of restaurants and bars. I asked John what he would like to do, and he said, 'Just grab a beer and lie by the pool. I'm feeling a bit tired.'

We got two sun loungers by the main pool and lay next to each other. After a few minutes I felt bored and asked John if he wanted a walk. He had his head buried in the John Grisham book he'd bought at the airport: a lawyer reading a book about lawyers. *A bit like coals to Newcastle*, I thought. John said, 'Not yet, thanks.'

My heart sank, and I had a strong feeling of sadness running down my body, all the way to the tips of my toes.

I got up, slid into the pool and swam over to the bar. I sat on one of the stools and ordered a fruit punch. A few minutes later, the blonde lady from breakfast swam up and asked if she could sit next to me. I said, 'Of course. Hi, I'm Rachel.' She introduced herself as Olivia and asked if I was enjoying it here.

We started talking about inconsequential stuff, and she seemed fun, with a warm smile and a lovely laugh. I asked if she had been here before and she told me it was their tenth anniversary, and that they'd come here ten years ago.

'Oh, have you been married for ten years?' I asked.

Olivia laughed and said, 'No, Richard and I have been married for thirty years.'

'Wow!' I said. 'What is the ten-year anniversary, then?'

'It's ten years since we started a new relationship.'

I was puzzled and said, 'I don't understand.'

Olivia laughed. 'It's a really long story. I'm sure you don't want to hear about it!'

'I would like to,' I said, 'because I've been thinking a lot about my own marriage recently.'

'OK, but do stop me when you've heard enough. In short, just over ten years ago we were about to split up after twenty years together, and then something happened that reconnected us and created a new and better relationship. We came out here to mark the beginning of a whole new chapter in our lives.'

'But I saw you this morning, and you seemed so much in love?' I said.

'Are you sure you want to hear about this?' Olivia laughed.

'Yes!' I said.

'Then I'll tell you.'

Chapter 6: Olivia's Story

'We had a great relationship, Richard and I, when we first met thirty years ago. We were very much in love and then life changed. I had my first child after three years. I loved my job as an air hostess, travelling the world, and suddenly I had to give that up and be a stay-at-home mummy. I love my three children very much, but for the seventeen years after the first child I lost myself and was playing a role that was not the real me. Richard was a great father, but he was developing his business, working long hours and getting quite stressed. It was crazy, because he was working really hard to give us a lovely home, but he never really had the time to enjoy it. So Richard and I drifted for years, and we didn't realise what was happening. We both knew we weren't really happy, but didn't understand why.' She paused. 'Can I ask you a question, Rachel?'

'Of course.'

'What score out of ten would you give your relationship when you first got married?'

'Absolutely a ten. I loved John very much and life was exciting.'

'And what score would you give it now?'

'Maybe a four. It's OK, but it isn't enough, and I'm often thinking, is this the best it's going to be from now on?'

'Yes, that's pretty similar to my score ten years ago.'

'So, what is your score now?'

'Right now, it's a ten. Sometimes, when life gets in the way, it does drop, but not for long as we both know how to get back on track and how important it is to deal with problems before they fester.'

'So, Olivia, please tell me more. What happened ten years ago, if you don't mind me asking?'

'OK. I will give you a quick summary after I've had another of these delicious cocktails. What will you have?'

'I'll have a banana daiquiri. At least that's got some fruit in it!'

'Sounds good! Let's work our way down the cocktail list! Or maybe not, as it will be lunchtime soon!' We both laughed, and Olivia turned to me. 'So, where was I? Oh, yes. For some years I knew I wasn't really happy and wanted more. Richard seemed unaware of my unhappiness, and we had lots of arguments over little things, and these just festered and were never resolved. In retrospect, these little things weren't the issue. What was bad was that we didn't talk about the important stuff and had lost sight of the fact we had to work at the relationship to make it grow. We assumed it would just stay as it had once been.

'Things got steadily worse. Richard got very ill and I started to fantasise about finding Mr Right, who would whisk me away. The reality was that we had three young children and needed to keep going for them. I managed to persuade Richard to come to marriage guidance. He was very reluctant, as he thought all I needed to do was to relax and find an outside interest. "After all," he said, "I do help with the children and the dishwasher."

'I booked a session – and we did see a counsellor after waiting over two months – but when we went along it didn't go well. Richard was very uptight and said very little. I just launched into everything that was wrong in my life and picked on Richard for the stuff he didn't do, including the fact we rarely had sex because I didn't enjoy it any more. I had hardly got into my stride when our hour was up.

'On the walk back to the car, Richard was very quiet. And on the drive home, he was so upset he was shaking, and said "I'm not going back there to be humiliated. If you want a divorce, then let's go and see a solicitor."

'I was shocked and started crying. I told Richard I did love him, but felt we had grown apart. We were very different people from when we first met and just didn't seem happy, or even seem to know each other.

'Richard turned off the main road and we headed down to the beach. He took my hand and led me to the sand dunes. We sat down looking out to sea, hearing the waves crash on the shore. It was a warm sunny day, but there was a strong wind and I was shivering. Richard looked me in the eyes and tears ran down his cheeks. He told me how much he loved me, how much I meant to him, and how he was terrified of losing me. He told me how unhappy he had been for several years, feeling unloved, unappreciated, and how he could do no right. He said he had come to dread walking into the house after a long day at work to be greeted by my face, which at best would be sad, and at worst would look at him as if he had done something wrong. Many times he said he felt like turning around and running away. He said his stress and illness had brought him to the realisation that he was terrified of dying a lonely, sad man, but didn't know what to do to change things.

'I held him close as he cried – it was the first time I had ever seen him really cry. He started sobbing and crying out with anguish. I felt so sad I had done this to the man I loved. In that moment, I felt reconnected to him. I held him even closer and kissed away his tears. I knew then, with searing certainty, he was the man I wanted to spend the rest of my life with; we just needed to work harder than we had ever worked before to make this right.

'We just held each other in our unhappiness, feeling connected by our despair. I started crying too, and told him I was sorry, but that I felt trapped and powerless. I asked him what we could do to resolve this. We told each other that we loved each other, and would find a way.

'We went back home, put on a brave face for the children, and decided that a long weekend away would be an opportunity to talk – and maybe even have some fun together. I arranged for my parents to come and look after the children and I booked a three-night trip to Prague. We both went with high hopes that something magical would happen. It was a lovely hotel in a beautiful city. We went to the museums, and sightseeing, but our meals together had awkward pauses...we didn't have anything to talk to each other about other than the children and how unhappy we were.'

Olivia smiled and said, 'It's OK, there is a happy ending. Can I have a quick swim and I'll finish?'

We both lowered ourselves into the water. I swam ten lengths and felt strangely excited at hearing Olivia's story, and also privileged to be let into the life of a stranger.

A fresh cocktail was waiting for me at the bar when I returned. 'You're a great swimmer,' Olivia said. 'I used to be competitive at school, but let all that go when I started work.' She took a sip of her drink. 'So, Prague was a bit of a disaster. We got back home, disappointed that life was back to normal...but normal just took over. I bought a few books on how to have a great relationship. Some were good; some were just full of American jargon. I did ask Richard to read one of them. *He did try* but nothing changed.

'I started doing some research, knowing we were unlikely to be able do this on our own, and that our past experience was not good. I came across a couple of therapists who looked very different and tried to persuade Richard to come along. He was very reluctant, again, and asked me how much it would cost and how long it would take. When I told him he laughed, but then looked thoughtful. He then said OK, but could he talk to them first. So he rang, spoke to the man for about thirty minutes, and said, "Alright, let's give it a try."

'So we went. The first session was very different from our previous experience. It lasted almost four hours, but just flew past. We both felt safe and able to express our feelings without blame. The two counsellors were brilliant at helping us to get it all out and to focus on what we really wanted.

'We had six sessions over four months. Each session was very different, and gave us the feeling that we were on a journey of discovery and of building something new. By the end, we felt like we were in a whole new and wonderful relationship. Looking back, it was quite magical, and I doubt if we would have stayed together if it was not for those two.

'Since then we have kept in touch with them, and gone back roughly once a year to make sure we are still on a good journey. So...it did have a happy ending, and life is great. Richard will be back from sailing soon, so I'm just going to go back to our room to freshen up for lunch.' Olivia then winked at me, and a big smile came onto her face. 'How would you like to have dinner with us this evening? We've booked at the Japanese restaurant. It's great fun.'

'That will be lovely!' I said.

'Great! About seven thirty?'

'Perfect. I'm looking forward to meeting Richard!'

I watched as Olivia gracefully slid off her stool and swam away.

Chapter 7: Something Has to Change - Rachel

I headed back to John. He was still deeply involved with his book and hardly looked up as I stood over him, with drops of water from my costume dripping onto his face.

'Hey!' he grumbled. 'Don't do that! You'll get my book wet!' He sat up and gave me a dirty look.

'I'm sorry,' I said. 'Would you liked to come back to the room before lunch?'

'No thanks,' he said. 'I'm happy reading my book.'

'I met a lovely lady who has invited us to join them for dinner in the Japanese restaurant tonight. Is that OK?'

'Oh...' John said. 'Is she on her own? I don't want her playing gooseberry.'

'No. Olivia is married to Richard. She's been telling me a fascinating story.'

'Oh, alright, I suppose so.' John turned back to his book.

I felt upset as I walked away. We had come to this beautiful place, to talk and see if we could get our relationship working again, and I was second place to a John Grisham novel. I stripped off and got into bed. I closed my eyes, feeling the effects of the alcohol. I started to think about Pierre, and felt myself moisten as I thought of him standing in front of me and slowly taking his kit off. My right hand moved down my body. A little voice in my head was telling me to stop, that this was all wrong. But a louder voice was telling me to carry on; I deserved an orgasm, and it had been a long time since the last one.

My hand continued down, and I felt the moisture and my clitoris start to engorge. My breathing deepened as I started to gently touch myself. I wished I'd brought my vibrator, but realised I could not let John know I had one; he would be furious, and I would be so embarrassed.

I thought of Pierre, fully undressed, felt his hardness against me as he started to gently remove my top and bra. He cupped my breasts in his hands and started to kiss my nipples and tease them with his tongue. I was feeling more aroused than I could remember. I imagined him gently laying me on the bed and very slowly pulling off my jeans and knickers. I lay there, feeling him kissing and licking my clitoris. My juices were flowing, and I was desperate to feel him inside me. I reached down and felt his wonderfully warm and large penis. I tried to pull him towards me, but he carried on licking and kissing me, and suddenly, without warning, I shouted out as I came to a huge, shuddering climax, writhing on the bed. The room felt like it was spinning, and I slowly opened my eyes and saw John, standing at the bottom of the bed, looking angry... and sad.

'What the fuck?' he shouted, and he stormed out of the room, slamming the door behind him.

Oh shit, I thought as I jumped out of bed, put my clothes on and tried to run after him. By the time I got out onto the path I couldn't see him, so walked disconsolately down to the beach, trying to avoid anyone seeing what must be a bright pink glow of embarrassment on my face.

I saw John standing there on his own, looking out to sea with the water up to his waist. I waded up to him and he turned around. I could see tears running down his cheeks, and he quickly turned away. I held him from behind and whispered into his ear, 'I'm sorry. I really need us to talk.'

He turned around. 'Are you having an affair?'

I was so shocked that I couldn't answer, and then said, 'No, I'm not.'

'I don't believe you. Why else won't you let me make love to you?'

'It's not that,' I said. 'There are lots of things that are wrong. We need to talk about us. I booked this holiday so we would have time to talk and be together. I did try and hint earlier that you might like to come up to the room, but you turned me down.'

'And what about this morning, when you turned me down?'

'Let's make time to try and talk about us; we are both upset and need to cool down.'

'I don't need to cool down.' He looked at me. 'At least I haven't been playing with myself.'

He then stormed off down the beach.

I went and sat on a sun lounger, closed my eyes and cried inside.

Chapter 8: Something has to Change - John

When we arrived at Grenada Airport it was hot, and it all seemed a bit chaotic. The taxi to the hotel was a bit old, and I hated the reggae music that was playing. It was a short drive, and when we headed through the gates it looked clean and well organised. The man on the gate was even wearing a uniform and had a revolver.

It was a long walk to our room, but when we got inside it was quite large with a huge bed and a view over to the pool, but I couldn't see the sea. I started unpacking my things, but Rachel told me to leave them and come for a swim. I hate leaving things undone. My shirts would get all creased, and my linen jacket would become unwearable. *Still*, I thought, *we are here so Rachel can sort herself out, so I better fall into line.*

We went down to the biggest pool and got into the water. I'm not a great swimmer, but quite liked the feeling of the warm water washing over me. I swam a couple of lengths and went over to the pool bar, where there were a number of people. Rachel was swimming up and down, so I ordered a large beer while I waited and picked at a few nuts that were in a bowl. I started to feel a bit more relaxed, but knew that after the month I'd had it would take several days for the stress to wash away. Rachel swam up, and as she stood up, and I saw the water droplets running off her bikini top, I thought how good she looked and started to feel a bit aroused.

I smiled at her and said, 'Thank you for arranging this. It is a good place.'

She smiled back at me, and I was surprised – it seemed like the first time for ages I had really seen her smile at me. *This is going to be good*, I thought.

I had a few more beers as Rachel worked her way down the list of cocktails. I prefer to know what it is I'm drinking, and don't like it when Rachel gets tiddly. She gets rather silly and flirts with other men. Still, it was looking hopeful as we went back to the room; but then Rachel spoiled the moment by saying we needed to go and eat before the restaurants closed. I thought we could order room service...afterwards...but that's not what she wanted, so I just went along with her plan.

We went to a restaurant, which had a buffet, which was OK. I was feeling pissed off that Rachel had rebuffed me, but was hoping that later we might make love. I tried to have a light conversation with her, and talk about the last few weeks at work, but she wasn't listening to me, so I stopped almost before I had started.

I had a few more beers, and Rachel got through most of a bottle of red wine. We went back to the room, and I was hoping she would have loosened up, but she decided she wanted a bath on the balcony. I thought this was a stupid idea, so while she was having a shower I logged onto the Wi-Fi and checked my emails. When I looked up she was fast asleep. Great, I thought as I got into bed, and turning my back on her I fell asleep.

The next morning, the sun was shining, and I was woken up by Rachel touching me on the shoulder and smiling at me. I turned and started to gently caress her nipple. I was shocked and quite angry when the bubble burst as she said, 'Ouch!' and pulled my hand off her. I thought, *Shit, this holiday is not going well*, but didn't want to say anything to start an argument so went and showered.

Breakfast was OK, but Rachel wasn't talking, so I thought it best to spend the morning just lying on the sunbed and waiting until her bad mood went. She went off to the bar and seemed to be in deep conversation with an older woman. How is it that women can talk so much about so little? I wondered, but was enjoying my book too much to really care...it really was fascinating to see the difference between the American and British legal systems.

I felt water dripping on my face and on the book. It was Rachel, with a silly smile on her face. She was already tiddly. She said something about going back to the room, to which I said, 'OK, I'll be there soon, after I've finished reading.' I was really getting into the book and thought that if Rachel was inviting me back for sex she would need to get herself ready, so I would have enough time.

I finished the chapter I was reading and headed back to the room with a spring in my step. As I opened the door, I could hear some strange noises inside, so I crept in and saw Rachel lying naked on the bed, groaning loudly and playing with herself. I held my breath and watched, surprised, shocked and horrified. Who was this person on our bed? She started shuddering, her eyes closed, and she shouted out. When she slowly opened her eyes she looked at me very strangely. I just had to leave the room. Is this why she didn't want to make love to me? What was she thinking, and who was she thinking about, and why was she never like that with me?

I ran to the beach and walked into the water. *Maybe I should just carry on walking*, I thought, *she clearly doesn't like me or even fancy me*. All I was there for was to pay for everything. I was sure she must be having an affair. It was the only reason. I started shaking and felt tears running down my cheeks. I heard my father's voice shouting at me, 'Big boys don't cry!' and I could see him glaring at me. I heard the boys at school laughing at me, too, and pointing at me and calling me 'Cissy'.

I felt a hand on my shoulder and turned around. It was Rachel. 'Are you having an affair?' I asked her.

She didn't reply straight away and had to think about it. She then said no, but I didn't believe her. I asked her why she didn't want to make love to me, and she couldn't answer. I had to get away, so I walked down the beach, as far from her as I could get.

It was getting hot, so I stopped at the beach bar and ordered a cool beer. I felt the anger building up inside of me, almost bursting out. How could I have been so stupid and not noticed?

Chapter 9: John Meets Richard

I slammed my empty beer glass down on the counter and asked for another. I saw a man on the other side of the bar glance at me with a concerned look on his face. *Shit*, I thought, *I hope he can't see that I've been crying.*

He walked around the bar and held out his hand. I shook it, but tried to avoid looking him in the face.

'Hi, I'm Richard,' the man said. 'Have you just arrived?'

'I'm John,' I replied. 'And yes, we arrived last night.'

'It's lovely here,' he said. 'There's so much to do and the food is great. Do you fancy a game of volleyball; there's a match about to start and we could do with a strong guy on our team?'

I told him that I wasn't very good and hadn't played for ages, that I was more of a rugby man, but he was gently persuasive and we walked the short distance to the court on the beach. There was a real mixture of men there, who all raised their hands and said hi, and the game started. It was hard work in the heat, but I started to get into the game and made a few good returns and even scored some points. We won 21-12, and it felt good to be part of a team as we sat at the bar afterwards drinking some beers.

The others left, and I was alone at the bar with Richard. 'You were good. Would you like to play tomorrow at the same time?' he asked.

I said I would.

'Are you OK?' he then asked. 'You were looking a bit down earlier.'

'I'm fine,' I said.

'Well, if you want to talk anytime, I'm around,' he offered, and he headed off.

Memories of seeing Rachel on the bed burst back into my head. I felt the tears starting again, so went back out onto the beach to sit where no one could see me. I thought about what I should do, and what I could do. I was trapped here for another thirteen days with someone who didn't love me; someone who was having an affair. I made up my mind that I couldn't share a room with Rachel. I would go and find another room and we would split up when we got back home.

I went to reception and asked if they had any spare rooms. The girl at reception looked a bit puzzled, and asked if there was anything wrong with our room. I said, 'No, it's fine. It's just that my wife snores a lot.' She had a look at the computer and said that there were no rooms available until next week, and added that she did have some earplugs if that would help?

She smiled as she handed me a packet of pink earplugs. I tried to say thank you and smile, but the words stuck in my throat as I walked away. What will I do? I wondered. Where will I sleep? I threw the earplugs into a waste bin.

I walked back to the room, steeling myself to see Rachel.

She was sitting on the bed looking anxious. She stood up, walked towards me and tried to smile. She put her arms around me, pulled me close. 'John, I have always been faithful to you and have never had an affair,' she said. 'Our relationship is not good and has to change for both of our sakes. Nothing though is going to change unless we can be honest and talk to each other.'

'Well, I don't know if I can believe you,' I said. 'You don't fancy me, and you don't want to make love to me. We don't have fun, and you are miserable and stroppy when I get home. I don't think you even like me.'

'There are lots of things that don't work for me, either. I was thinking that maybe we should call it a day, but a story I heard this morning made me think there could be hope. We have three lovely kids and eighteen years of investment that I'm not walking away from.'

'So what's the story?' I asked.

'You'll hear it later,' Rachel said.

'What do you mean?'

'I told you earlier, by the pool, but I don't think you were listening properly. I met a lady this morning, and she told me about how her relationship had recovered from being in a really bad place.'

'I hope you haven't told her about us!' I said angrily.

'No, I haven't,' Rachel said. 'She just started telling me how happy she was and how her life changed ten years ago. It's a wonderful story. Anyway, we are meeting for dinner. We don't have to talk about anything personal. We are booked for the Japanese restaurant at seven thirty.'

'Oh,' I said. 'I can't say I'm that keen. I will give it a go, but I really don't want to share our private stuff with strangers.'

'I'm going for a bath on the balcony, would you like to join me?'

'No thanks,' I said. 'I'm just going to read.'

I lay on the bed and picked up my book. I couldn't focus on John Grisham's words; I was seething inside and feeling picked on by Rachel. I worked really hard to provide for the family but seemed to get nothing in return. Why was life so unfair?

I lay there half in and half out of my book. I could hear the water running in the big tub on the balcony and wondered how on earth Rachel could lie there in full view of everyone. The water stopped running and I heard her get into the bath. Then it went quiet.

After a few minutes, curiosity got the better of me and I went to the doors and peeped out onto the balcony. There were curtains around the outside that had been closed for privacy and Rachel had lit some candles. She was lying there up to her neck in bubbles. I could see her eyes glistening in the candlelight. It looked like she was crying. She turned, glanced at me, and looked away.

I had a sense of something strange growing in my chest; like a warm rush of blood from my heart melting what felt like ice surrounding it. I walked over to Rachel, bent down and started kissing the tears on her cheeks. I then put my hand gently under her chin and kissed her on the lips. I felt something I hadn't experienced for many years, a sense of love and desire, and my emotions crept outside the fortress of ice and stone I had built and started to connect with Rachel's emotions. Rachel, my wife, the person I had forgotten I loved. I stripped off my swimming shorts and t-shirt and climbed into the large bath. Rachel looked shocked as I knelt down astride her, put my arms around her and held her close to me. I looked her in the eyes and sensed something passing between us. My lips opened and, almost without realising it, the words burst out from inside of me: 'Rachel, I love you.'

She put her arms around me and held me tight. She cried. Minutes passed. I let go and sat at the other end of the bath. Tears were still falling, but the look on her face was different, softer, and had the beginnings of a smile.

'Thank you,' she said. 'I haven't heard those words for so long.' She then reached out with her right hand and stroked my leg. 'Maybe there is some hope for us.'

Rachel's right foot moved forward, between my legs, and I could feel her toes gently exploring my groin. I started to feel aroused, and my body started to tense in surprise. She leaned forward, and her right hand travelled up my thigh, all the way up my thigh, further up, until she gently grasped my penis and started to squeeze. I saw her smile, and I relaxed and leaned further back. She started to stroke me, up and down, slowly at first, and then a little faster. I got harder and groaned in unexpected pleasure. I wanted to get back in control, but decided just to relax and enjoy the ride. This was really surprising; something I did not remember her ever doing. Our love-making had always been fairly conventional, with me in control, and all spontaneity had faded away many years ago.

I realised I was getting very close to orgasm, but was not doing anything, just letting Rachel do all the hard work...but put those thoughts aside as I could no longer hold back and let out a loud groan as I exploded into her hand. Rachel smiled at me and said, 'I think that is one-all!'

I felt embarrassed, but burst out laughing. I laughed like I hadn't in ages, and felt the tension and anger run away. I then looked at Rachel and said, 'Wow.'

She stroked my hand. 'Thank you for joining me,' she said. 'Shall we go to dinner?'

'OK,' I said. 'And, thank you; that was rather nice.'

Rachel smiled and winked. 'Let's go, then.'

I walked back inside feeling so much lighter. I dried myself off and dressed in a pair of trousers and a shirt. Rachel was busy in the bathroom putting makeup on, so I sat and waited. When she emerged she was wearing a dress I hadn't seen before, and looked at herself in the mirror.

'You look amazing,' I said. 'Is that a new dress?'

'Yes,' she said. 'It was reduced.'

'Oh, good,' I said.

Rachel put on some lipstick and glanced at her watch. 'Let's go. Olivia and Richard will be waiting for us in the restaurant.'

She held out her hand and smiled at me. I took it, and felt a buzz running up my arm. I felt nervous, like I was on my first date.

We walked along the paths, which were lit up, and I could hear the cicadas doing whatever it is they do at night. There was a fresh smell of flowers, plants and the sea. Rachel led me to the door of a restaurant called Kimono's. I stopped.

'It's OK, they won't bite!' Rachel said, and we stepped inside.

Chapter 10: Richard's Story - Rachel

It was dark inside and decorated with Japanese murals. I could feel that John was nervous. I was surprised at what had just happened, but felt excited I had broken out of the mould and had created a new connection with him.

I saw Olivia at a corner table. She caught my eye and waved. We walked over to a large square table with a big space in the centre. Olivia stood up, as did the handsome, older man next to her. She reached out and gave me a hug, which I was surprised at, but it felt good.

'Rachel, this is Richard, my husband,' she said.

Richard smiled, held out his hand and shook mine. 'Hello,' he said. 'Lovely to meet you.'

'Are you going to introduce me?' Olivia asked me.

'I'm sorry, this is John,' I said as they shook hands, John looking a bit stiff.

He turned to look at Richard. 'Hello,' he said, with a bit of a smile.

'Hello, volleyball star! It's good to see you again!'

'Do you know each other?' I asked in surprise.

'Yes, we played volleyball this afternoon,' John answered.

'Come and sit down and I'll explain what happens,' Olivia then said. 'It's great fun.' We sat down at the table. 'This is a real show,' she continued. 'In a few minutes, the teppanyaki chef will appear. He cooks beef, chicken, fish and prawns in front of us in a very unusual way. We came here last week, and it was brilliant.'

'Great!' I said, and looked at John, who seemed a bit more relaxed.

The waitress came and took our orders for drinks. Olivia said, 'Let's celebrate first,' and ordered a bottle of Prosecco to be followed by a bottle of Malbec and a Sauvignon Blanc. The drinks came quickly, and the waitress poured the fizz. Olivia raised her glass and said, 'Here's to love and the future!'

John appeared surprised, but turned to me, smiled, and raised his glass.

The chef appeared in front of us with a flourish. He started his show of juggling sharp knives and then throwing eggs around. We watched, spellbound, and started to laugh as the Prosecco eased its way into our systems. The first course appeared, and the conversation between the four of us started to flow. I even heard John laugh a few times. Then the chef got to work on the hot stones, whilst keeping up a stream of jokes and juggling, and I breathed in the smell of the food and herbs and spices. The food was delicious, and we worked our way through several bottles of wine.

I was feeling very full and relaxed as the meal finished, and Richard asked if we would like to join them for a nightcap, so we walked, a bit unsteadily, down to the bar by the beach. The moon was almost full and bathing the tranquil sea in its soft light. We sat at a round table and Richard returned with four large glasses on a tray. 'Here's the cocktail of the day,' he said. 'It's got rum and fruit, so it's good for you.'

It tasted wonderful, but strong!

'Olivia said she spoke to you earlier and told you a bit about us,' Richard continued. 'I just wanted to say we were in a very sad and difficult place ten years ago, but I am now with the woman I love unconditionally, and it is remarkable just how much things have changed. My hope is that we can pay forward to others some of what we learned, because to love and be loved is the most precious gift.'

Richard paused, looking serious and thoughtful. He glanced at Olivia, and then leaned over to give her a kiss on the cheek.

'I'm not sure what you have heard about our story, so let me give you my summary and tell you what changed.

'I fell in love with Olivia when we first met thirty years ago. I was flying out to Japan to meet a supplier and she was this beautiful air hostess serving me with drinks. I remember the tingle when she touched my fingers when passing me my drink. In the two weeks I was out in Japan, I fantasised about her, which was crazy, because she was way out of my league and I didn't even know her name.

'On the flight back, fate played its part and Olivia was on duty, and we talked a bit. When I was getting off the plane at Heathrow, I plucked up courage and gave her my business card as she was saying farewell to the passengers. I expected nothing and was amazed when she rang me the next week, inviting me to a party in South Kensington. I went along in a complete dream. The flat was full of half-drunk hostesses and pilots, and I felt like a fish out of water; and then Olivia appeared from the kitchen, came up to me, and reached up to kiss me on the cheeks. I almost passed out with excitement.'

Richard smiled, took a big swallow of his cocktail, and continued. 'Well, to cut a long story short, it was a real whirlwind romance. Olivia was still jetting off around the world, and I was building up my IT business from just me to what is now a large company, but we moved in together. Olivia got pregnant earlier than planned and Ami arrived twenty-seven years ago, followed by Kate who is now twenty-five, and Mark who is twenty-one. Olivia loved her job, but had to leave it to bring up the children. And I was working hard to provide a comfortable life for us all.

'The truth is, we started to have lots of arguments about little things. And it got to the stage where I would stay late at work because I was fed up with coming home to yet another argument, so I would time things so I got back when Olivia was in bed asleep and got up before she woke. I only saw the kids at the weekend, and that wasn't much fun because we seemed to have less and less in common. It was bizarre that I was working so hard to pay for the upkeep of a home that I spent little time in, and funded the lives of four people I felt so disconnected from.

'I was sleepwalking into misery. I felt stressed and really unhappy. Things came to a head ten years ago when I started to get shooting pains in my chest and down my left arm. These got worse and worse until, one night, when I got home, I was sitting in the chair and had an enormous pain. I flinched and went grey. Olivia looked at me, wondering why I was making a strange noise and asked me what was wrong. I couldn't really speak. I remember the look of disdain on her face quickly changing to concern. She felt my pulse and called an ambulance.

'The paramedics turned up very quickly and I got the full blue-light experience, being whisked into the cardiac ward. They kept me in for a week and ran all sorts of scans and tests. Olivia and the kids came to see me every day; but it was like having strangers coming to see me, with awkward pauses, and none of us able to say what we really felt. I was sad to realise I had been losing them, and might have lost them completely. I visualised my funeral, and wondered who would be there and what they would say about me. At the end of the week, the consultant came around. He told me my heart was fine, and it was probably stress that had caused the intense pain, and that I could go. "Oh, and by the way," he added, "You could do with losing a stone or more and doing some exercise!"

'What was really bizarre was that I felt disappointed; disappointed I wasn't given a magic pill and that I would have to find my own solution. But I have always been good at managing projects, so set myself a new project of sorting my life out. I broke it down into four categories: work, body, mind and family.

'I decided I needed to recruit a PA, too, as well as an operations manager to take over the mundane stuff that I had been escaping into. I started cycling and eating more healthily. Sorting out my mind was harder, but I booked myself into a Buddhist meditation retreat, which got me started on regular meditation which I found cleared my mind of all the stuff that had been clogging up my thoughts.

'It is interesting that "family" was last on my list, but that involved other people, so was more difficult, as I had no control over them. I was busy sorting my own life out and Olivia got neglected. She dragged me along to marriage counselling. We had to wait months for the appointment, and when we went it seemed like most of the first session was an opportunity for Olivia to have a go at me. I refused to go back. On the drive home, I stopped at the beach and just broke down in tears of despair. But Olivia and I talked properly for the first time in years, said we loved each other but were trapped in a very bad place. We vowed to change things.

'We booked a long weekend in Prague, which should have been lovely, but we'd carried our confusion and despair with us. We got back, and life was the same. Olivia bought a lot of books on relationships, and I read one of them. I discovered that being told someone else's answers didn't help when it seemed impossible to break out of the sad place we were both in.

Olivia did some research, and we went to see a couple of therapists who were very different. Their focus was on helping us achieve the outcomes we wanted. They helped us to understand something called The Relationship Paradigm. Over a few months they led us onto a different path, of leaving the past behind and creating a whole new relationship. It was the best thing we have ever done, as it transformed our lives. We do need to check our progress and have input sometimes, but the last ten years have been better than I could ever have dreamed were possible.'

'Wow,' I said, 'that is a wonderful story. I would love to understand more. What do you think, John?'

'Hmmm,' John said. 'I would like to, but I'm not sure how relevant it is for us...'

'I'm happy to tell you more, John. Maybe tomorrow, before volleyball?' Richard offered.

John nodded. 'OK,' he said, but there was a deep frown across his brow.

'Thank you, both,' I said. 'It has been a wonderful evening, and

I really appreciate your openness. It's so good to hear your story. I'm sure we could learn a lot from it.'

Richard raised his glass and said, 'Here's to your future. We are around for the next few days and would love to talk some more, maybe when we are a bit more sober.'

John and I walked back to our room. The smell of the flowers was gorgeous, and the moonlight was showing the way along the paths. I reached out and took John's hand. I felt a sense of connection, and that he was thinking things through. I let the silence take its place, feeling that hope had appeared on that day.

We got back to the room and undressed slowly. John got into bed with me, still silent. He reached out and held me close. I could hear the sound of his breathing and felt his thoughts flowing. He started to stroke my back and told me he loved me. We fell asleep in each other's arms.

Chapter 11: Rollercoaster - John

I woke up to see Rachel in my arms asleep. I looked at her face and felt a wonderful warmth filling my body. Her eyes slowly opened. When she saw me she startled, and then smiled. I held her closer and kissed her on the lips. It felt like my heart was about to burst out of my chest, and I threw aside reservations and habits and slid under the sheet and started to gently kiss her right breast. Her nipple started to firm up and she started to move her legs apart. I moved to her left breast. It was lovely, but different, and I teased her nipple with my tongue and lips. It felt like Rachel was coming alive in a way I could not remember, and I slowly moved down her body, doing things that felt both strange and very natural. Rachel was beginning to writhe gently, and it felt good.

I threw off the sheets and moved further down. I started to caress her clitoris with my tongue. The taste was unusual but so good. I had a moment where I felt so aroused I just wanted to enter her and come, but I put those thoughts aside and concentrated on giving Rachel pleasure. I could feel her clitoris grow, which was something I had never noticed before. But then when you're on top, and a few feet away, it would be difficult to see. I had another moment of distraction as I wondered what sex had been like for Rachel for the last eighteen years; but then got back into the moment and, with an almost naïve delight, just explored the undiscovered territory before me – and if the groans and movements were anything to go by, Rachel was enjoying it rather a lot. She then started to shudder, and the groans grew louder. With a sudden roar, she arched her back, shouted 'Oh God!' and fell back onto the bed.

I stopped and looked at her; she was flushed in the face and smiling, and said, 'Two-one!'

I lay next to her and heard her breathing subside. She turned to me and said, 'Thank you, that was amazing. Where have you been for the last eighteen years?'

I didn't reply, but just lay there soaking in the moment and hoping that my turn would come next. After waiting for a while, I said, 'What shall we do now?'

'I'm happy to go and have breakfast and then relax. Richard said something to you about having a talk, before volleyball?'

'Oh yes,' I said. 'I'm not sure I need to now.'

'I think you should,' Rachel said. 'It will be good for you to hear his story; after all, I've heard Olivia's.'

'Maybe,' I said, suddenly feeling under pressure, the heady afterglow of pleasuring Rachel fading fast. 'Let's go and have some breakfast.'

I went to have a shower and walked back in the room to see Rachel still lying in bed, dozing. 'Come on,' I said. 'I'm starving.'

'OK, give me a minute,' she replied, and turned on her side.

I felt a bit frustrated, as it seemed she was back in control and I wasn't being listened to. I got dressed quickly, picked up my book and went onto the balcony. The sun was warm, and I could hear splashing from the nearby pool. I started to think that this would be an expensive holiday unless we used the facilities and got the best out of our time. If we didn't, it would be money wasted.

I started reading my book again, but felt distracted and a bit grumpy. I put it down and went back into the room. I could hear Rachel gently snoring and agonised over whether to wake her or not. I decided to leave her be and, feeling a bit of a martyr, headed down for breakfast. It was strange just how quickly things changed. Maybe the bit about feeling in love with Rachel again was just an illusion, and things would go back to normal when we returned home.

I got outside and the sun, the light, the openness, the sounds and smells hit me. I slowed down my pace and stopped. I realised

I didn't know what I was doing. I felt upset with Rachel, but didn't know why. I realised that if I carried on, I would be putting more distance between us and that we needed to sort this out. I turned around and headed back to the room. Rachel was still asleep, so I sat down on the edge of the bed, unsure what to do. I was frozen by indecision. I felt her stir and she rolled over. 'What's the time?' she said. 'Did I fall asleep?' She smiled a sleepy smile at me and reached out her hand and stroked my back. 'Do you want to come back to bed?'

I thought through my choices and realised that although I was hungry for breakfast, that could maybe wait. Uncertain about what would happen and how I was feeling, I climbed into bed. Rachel put her arms out to me and held me close.

'This last day has been a real rollercoaster,' she said, 'but some nice things have happened, and we seem to have broken through the ice. I'm not sure where we are going, but at least we are moving somewhere.'

'Yes,' I said, 'but I'm confused. I don't know what is happening, and I'm not sure how I really feel. I'm worried that all this is just because we are on holiday, and when we get back home it will be life as it was before, which I now realise wasn't great.'

Rachel gave me a squeeze and said, 'Yes, there is lots to talk about but, for the moment, can you just try and enjoy where we are and try and have some fun?'

'OK,' I said. 'I'm still starving.'

Rachel looked a bit disappointed and said, 'I'll get dressed then.'

She got out of bed and went into the bathroom. What was that all about?

Some minutes later she came into the bedroom, got dressed into shorts and a t-shirt and said, 'Let's go.'

I didn't understand how one minute she could be so close and the next quite cold. I found her moodiness really difficult to cope with. I followed her out of the door and we headed down the path to the restaurant to get breakfast.

We went to a different restaurant, where there was a big buffet display. We were shown to a table overlooking the pool. The air conditioning made the room cool, but the glance Rachel gave me was even colder.

'What's wrong?' I said.

'Nothing,' Rachel replied, and stood up to go and help herself to breakfast.

Fuck it, I thought, and went to load up my plate with food.

We ate in silence, and I kept going back to the buffet to help myself to more food.

'Do you really need all that?' Rachel asked.

'Yes, I'm starving, and it's all included, so at least I'm getting value,' I snapped.

Rachel looked at me sadly and said, 'I think I'll go and have a sail this morning. Would you like to come?'

'No,' I said. 'You know I hate small boats.'

'OK, I'll see you at lunch.'

She stood up and walked off, leaving me fuming at the table.

I saw Olivia and Richard walk by, holding hands and looking happy. Seeing them gave me a strange mix of annoyance and jealousy.

Richard came over and said, 'Hello, John. It was a great meal last night. How are you doing today?'

'Alright,' I said. 'Rachel is going sailing this morning.'

'Would you like to keep me company on a walk?' Richard asked.

'I'm not sure...'

'Please? I would appreciate it.'

'OK. When are you going?'

'About ten minutes, once I've got properly dressed,' Richard confirmed.

'Are you sure you want me to come?' I asked him.

'Yes, I am,' said Richard. 'I will see you down here soon.'

I poured another coffee, puzzled that he was being so friendly. It seemed more than a casual holiday friendship... So, what was in it for him?

But what had I got to lose? Life with Rachel, and what the future might feel like, seemed uncertain and scary, so I waited for him to return.

Chapter 12: John Opens Up to Richard

I was sitting there drinking coffee and feasting on the almost endless supply of Danish pastries when Richard returned. He smiled at me, which I found annoying. I thought, *Why is he so bloody happy?*

Richard sat down next to me and said, 'This isn't easy for me, and is probably even harder for you, but I sense you might be where I was ten years ago and wanted to offer you the opportunity to learn from my mistakes. If you want to have a walk and talk about rugby, I am very happy to do that. It would be good to get a bit of exercise while Olivia and Rachel are out conquering the waves. What do you think?'

'I really appreciate the offer,' I said. 'Let's have a walk and talk about rugby and see what happens. As long as we are back in time for volleyball.'

We walked down to the beach. I could feel the warmth of the sun on my face and wished I had a hat with me. Richard was quiet, and I began to think this had been a mistake. We headed to the right, past the diving school and up onto the clifftop path. I was still feeling a bit uncertain and embarrassed, when Richard broke the silence.

'I told you a bit about our story last night,' he said. 'I've become very passionate about what we learned ten years ago, and what got us from a relationship on the brink of collapse to one that is wonderful. Every day I'm thankful for what I now know as, without that, life would have been very different for our family. When I come across couples who might be in a similar place to where we were, I want to reach out and give them the opportunity to change, as we did. I do believe there is nothing more important in life than a great, loving relationship and, every day, I thank whoever is up there for what I have.

'I hope I don't sound like I am preaching, but I have been given this incredible gift and want others to have it too. If I'm talking rubbish, or you don't want to hear, just say and I will keep quiet.'

'Thank you, Richard, I do appreciate your openness, but I find it strange and uncomfortable to open up in the way in which you have.'

'It was hard for me, too,' Richard admitted. 'I used to keep my feelings very close to my chest. I was brought up to believe that real men didn't show feelings, because it was a sign of weakness. It took what I thought was a heart attack to realise that all those bottled up feelings were killing me and were starving Olivia and the kids of life, too. Being able to express how I really feel and to facilitate others doing the same has made me a much better businessman, boss, husband and father.'

'Really? I have always thought men showing feelings were frowned on. That's something I was taught by my dad, and on the rugby pitch. I'm not sure I could do that.'

'So, John, on a scale of one to ten, how happy are you right now?'

'About four,' I said. 'It has gone from one to eight several times since we got here, and before we got here it was about four, on average.'

'So, what would you like to have happen?'

That's a weird question to ask, I thought as we walked along, the beautiful blue sea on my left and the sun on my face. 'I would like to work less hard, be appreciated more by the family, and for Rachel to do her fair share and have more fun.'

'How do you think you might achieve that?'

'I've no idea. I was hoping this holiday would get Rachel back into a good place.'

'I learned that the way I was being with Olivia was damaging my life. I had put all the blame on her and given her responsibility for making my life better. She was doing the same, and we were trapped in a vicious spiral of blame.'

'Oh,' I said, mulling over how I was feeling.

'Things only started to improve when I became clear about what I wanted, and what Olivia wanted, and took responsibility for myself rather than blaming others.'

'That is easy to say, but how difficult is that to do?' I asked.

'It's as difficult as you want to make it,' Richard replied. 'It requires you to let go of your ego and focus on what is really important to you. How much would it be worth for your happiness to go from four to be consistently nine or ten?'

I found it awkward to be asked these questions by a person I hardly knew, but also surprisingly good, because Richard felt like someone I could trust and be open with.

'It would be worth an awful lot,' I said. 'It's difficult to put a value on it, but it sounds a bit like winning the lottery: it's never going to happen.'

'It certainly won't unless you buy a ticket!' Richard laughed.

'Hmm...' I said. 'So what would I need to do?'

'The starting point is to be very clear about what is wrong with your life and your relationship at the moment. Then you need to be certain about what you do want. Only then can you decide whether it is worth investing the time and effort in making things better. But it's not a one-off investment. You have to keep working at it.'

I thought this through as I looked out to sea. I could see a few small dinghies hurtling along in the warm breeze. I wondered if Rachel was out there.

'When you told us your story last night there were a lot of parallels with mine,' I said. 'Rachel and I got together at university and got married about fourteen years ago, when she got pregnant. Life was pretty good for a few years, but then Jenny was born two years later and was a difficult baby. Rachel had to give up work, and suddenly I'd gone from junior solicitor to being on the path to becoming a partner, so I could earn enough to pay for the wife, kids and big house. Fun got forgotten and I became the sole breadwinner. I just assumed that was what I had to be and put up with it.

'We never really talked about how we were feeling and started to argue over stuff. I also got fed up with coming home late every night and not feeling appreciated or understood. That has continued until just over a month ago, when I decided enough was enough. So we came on holiday so that Rachel could have some time to get her head straight.' I paused, feeling embarrassed. 'Since we got here it's been a hell of a rollercoaster, and I don't know where we stand, whether she is having an affair or what. One minute she's all over me and the next I'm rejected.'

'I can understand,' said Richard. 'I went through the same. I even hired a private detective because I thought Olivia must be having an affair, but he said she wasn't. When a couple drift apart they create all sorts of thoughts to try and make sense of a world that has changed and that they no longer understand.'

'I feel like I'm living in a world I don't recognise; like I've been sleepwalking through the last eighteen years and have woken up to realise that all of the hard work has led me nowhere.'

Richard stopped walking and looked at me. 'Almost everyone I have met in the last ten years has said the same to me. The thing is, you now have a choice to make. I can't really help you with that choice; all I can do is make you aware of the possibilities.'

'So, where do I start?' I said.

'Let's finish our walk and then join the volleyball match. If you can put up with another dinner, Olivia and I will talk you both through the relationship paradigm and then let you choose what to do with it. I run an IT company, and have learned a lot about relationships, but I would rather leave the detail to the professionals.'

'OK, that sounds like a good plan,' I said. 'Shall we go to the headland and then head back?'

We strode on, my mind whirling in a mixture of excitement and dread. Excitement about being able to sort things out, and dread that it might not work and I might end up being very disappointed.

The sun was hot, but the wind was cool up here; and the scenery was stunning, with blue seas dotted with yachts, and rugged cliffs. We soon got to the headland, from where we could see the capital, St Georges, in the distance.

We walked back in companionable silence. By the time we got back to the resort it was almost lunchtime.

'See you at volleyball at three,' Richard said.

I walked along the beach to where the dinghies were kept, and watched as a familiar figure sailed back to the beach and Olivia came to a graceful stop. I then saw Rachel heading in. She tried to stop her boat and fell out backwards with a splash. One of the boat boys ran out to grab the dinghy and help her out. She was laughing, and said to Olivia, 'You won!'

Rachel saw me and came over. 'That was great!' she said. 'I'm a bit rusty, though. I'll go and get changed and then let's have lunch.'

We met at the beach bar for lunch. I was still feeling a bit full after my pig out on breakfast and Danish pastries and just had a burger, fries and a beer. Rachel, eating her seafood salad, talked excitedly about the race she'd had with Olivia and asked how I got on. I told her Richard and I had walked and talked, and that he offered to meet up for dinner to give us the full works.

Rachel asked me how I was feeling. I said, 'I'm not sure. I'm feeling confused.'

'Do you want to have dinner with them?'

'They seem a nice couple, but they're a bit like Jehovah's Witnesses, wanting to convert us!'

'Well, if it helps get us to a better place, that will be well worth it.'

'OK,' I said, feeling a bit pressured.

'I'm going to go and do some girly things this afternoon while you play volleyball,' she then said. 'See you in the room later.'

I met Richard for volleyball, where our team won four matches and lost one. I played pretty well. I was feeling exhausted and slumped at the bar, enjoying a large, cool beer. The other players were laughing and enjoying the atmosphere and the drinks. I felt a glow of satisfaction and told Richard we would like to meet them for dinner.

'That's great. How about the French restaurant at about 8.00pm?'

'Great,' I said, and headed back to the room.

The lights were out, but there was a flickering of candlelight from the balcony. Rachel was in a bath full of bubbles with a glass of fizz in her hand.

'Hi,' she said. 'Come and join me?'

'OK, move up,' I said and started to take my clothes off, before realising that the curtains were open and we might be seen.

'It's OK,' Rachel said. 'We can't be seen, and anyway, it's a lovely view.'

I climbed wearily into the bath. Rachel picked up an empty glass and the bottle of fizz and passed them to me. 'Well done,' she said. 'I never knew you were a volleyball star.'

'I'm not really,' I said. 'But it was fun.'

I lay there in the warmth of the bath, feeling the alcohol relax me. I started to worry about dinner and whether I was becoming too vulnerable.

'Richard said they will meet us in the French restaurant at eight. Is that OK?'

'Yes, that's great. I'm sure it will be interesting.'

'Hmm...' I said as I poured another glass of fizz.

Chapter 13: Olivia Explains - Rachel

I lay in the bath watching John, not sure what he was thinking or feeling. I reflected on the last two days. There had been some good moments and some fun, but it felt very brittle; it didn't take much for John to go off in a huff or to disengage. I still wasn't sure I really wanted to be with him or whether he had the commitment to try to make the relationship work.

He saw me watching, looked embarrassed and turned his head away; but I carried on looking at him, realising he was now a bit of a stranger and a very different person to the John I met eighteen years ago. It felt like I had gone to sleep and woken up in a very different place with different people. The life I thought I knew had gone and I had to make up my mind what I wanted my life to be in the future. I felt a chill of fear running down my head into my spine. I shivered deeply, closed my eyes and concentrated on my feelings. What was I really scared of? I realised with blinding clarity that my fear was of being stuck in a relationship that had become loveless, with a man I no longer knew, and in a routine that was suffocating. I felt the cold pass down through my body... but then sensed a warmth rising up from my heart, so strong it made me gasp. I had the sense of this warmth being like a rising sun, creating new possibilities that could be exciting and really fulfilling. It felt really good and I felt powerful; I no longer needed to be a passenger in this life; I could steer my own course.

I opened my eyes and saw John looking puzzled.

'Are you OK?' he said. 'You were twitching.'

'I'm fine. I was just thinking.'

'OK...' John said, and looked away.

I felt it was important to not let this moment pass. There needed to be more truth spoken. We needed to express our feelings and avoid hiding in the cloud of mediocrity.

'Actually, John,' – the words rushed out – 'I was thinking and feeling about us. I'm afraid of staying stuck where we are, but realise we have the opportunity to create something much better, which feels good. I was looking at you and thinking that I don't really know you now. It's the first time for many years I've looked closely at you and realised you are so different...we are both so different from when we first met eighteen years ago.

'I know we cannot go on as we are. The future is uncertain, but has to be better than where we have got to. Big change is needed and I really want it to happen. Where that will take us is uncertain, and scary, but also exciting. We need to talk, to share and to work together to see if we can change enough.

'If we want our relationship to last, we have to fight for it. I don't know how, but meeting Olivia and Richard feels like it has opened a door to possibilities. We just need to decide if we are brave enough to go through that door, because if we don't then we will be going through different and separate doors.'

John just looked at me.

'John, this is about fighting for us. Are you going to give up without even trying? If you were on the rugby field, and at half time were losing badly, would you just give up and not bother going on for the second half, or would you dig deep, encourage the others and head back onto the pitch with your head held high knowing you would do your very best?'

John smiled. 'Wow! You've missed your vocation as a rugby coach!'

'John...'

'You're right, but this is very strange and difficult for me. I'm scared because I don't feel in control. It feels like the bubble has burst and I'm standing on a stage naked and can't see who is in the audience.'

'Maybe we are going to have to be truly naked with each other,' I said. 'Talk about stuff we haven't ever done and express our feelings. It's going to be an interesting experience, but I hope it will get us out of this rut. Maybe Olivia and Richard will help us find the right door. It does seem more than coincidence that they have appeared in our life at just the right moment.'

'Hmm, let's see how it goes, but I don't want to be naked in front of them. I'm not comfortable talking to strangers about our personal stuff.'

'Yes, let's see how it goes,' I said.

I smiled at him and started to get out of the bath. He reached out and held my arm. 'I do love you,' he said. 'I do want to make this work, for you, for me, and for the kids.'

'Thank you.' I leant down and kissed him on the top of the head. 'Dinner and the doorways beckon!'

I looked at the clock. It was almost 8.00pm!

We both dressed quickly, and John tentatively took my hand as we walked down the path. I could smell the cooling air and the scents of the flowers. I could also sense John's uncertainty. I was worried about what the evening would bring, as well as where the next ten days would take us. I did feel we had crossed a bridge, however, and was aware of a tingle of excitement about the future.

We found our way to the restaurant and walked into a cool, dimly lit room with each table bathed in candlelight. It seemed designed to be romantic, and a strange place to talk about relationship problems.

I saw Olivia at a table in the corner of the restaurant. She was talking animatedly to Richard, and then stopped, and they both burst out laughing, which made me wonder: When did either of us really laugh?

Olivia then saw me and waved. She was still laughing when we got to the table. 'Don't mind us, we were just sharing a story from my school days, about my first appearance in a school play. Come and join us.'

Richard leapt up, shook John's hand and gave me a gentle hug. Olivia gave me a big hug and then gave John a kiss on both cheeks.

'Have a look through the menu. The food here was wonderful when we ate here a few days ago. What would you like to drink? We thought we would start off with some champagne?'

'That sounds good,' said John as he sat down next to Richard.

'Great!' I said. Olivia ordered champagne from the waiter, and I sat and studied the menu, which only had a few choices but sounded delicious. 'I can't get over the fact all this is included!' I said. 'It seems a shame not to drink and eat to excess!'

'Enjoy it while you can,' said Olivia.

We all ordered and talked about inconsequential stuff. Olivia and I explained the fun we'd had sailing, and John and Richard talked about the volleyball and their success that afternoon.

Soon there was a pause in the conversation. Olivia looked at Richard; she then looked at us. 'Would you like us to tell you a bit more about our story and what changed our lives all those years ago? I know it seems a bit strange talking about this in such a lovely place, so full of love, fun and light, but we are really passionate about the difference it made to us and want to pass this on to others.'

I glanced at John, who was looking thoughtful and a bit worried.

'Yes, please, we would love to hear more. I really appreciate your openness and generosity, but must admit that to have relative strangers telling us all their personal stuff is a bit strange,' John said.

'Yes,' Olivia acknowledged. 'Ten years ago I would have found it very weird too, but we have learned the importance of communication and openness. We are delighted that you are open to listening.' She smiled at Richard. 'Richard, please join in if you want to,' she said, and he nodded.

'OK, here goes. As we have described, ten years ago we were in a really bad place, and our relationship had hit the bottom without us realising it. We tried marriage counselling, but this seemed to make things worse as it drove us further apart, with us blaming each other. Richard had been focused on his business to make money to support the family and make us happy. I had been focused on the children and was resentful of having had to give up my fun career. I was also increasingly angry that Richard seemed wedded to the business and that our time together was short and not much fun. I kept wondering if this was what I had really signed up for, and how long I could put up with it before I exploded. Richard, is that a fair summary?'

'Yes, it is,' Richard agreed. 'I had a different perspective, but I came to understand Olivia's too. I was in a really bad place and, at times, felt suicidal. I had put all my efforts into growing the business to earn the money to give Olivia and the kids what they wanted – a lovely house and expensive holidays – but the price of all that was I had no time with them, and the expensive holidays were miserable because we were arguing all the time. I felt resentful and unappreciated, and things seemed to be getting worse and worse. I knew this could not continue.'

'Gosh, that must have been difficult for both of you,' I said. 'There are a lot of similarities to our position. What happened, then, because you seem in a great place now?'

'I bought lots of books on how to have a great relationship,' said Olivia. 'A few of them made sense, but some were too simplistic or written as "Do what I say". I did try talking to Richard about what I'd been reading, but we were both trapped behind our walls of resentment and blaming each other. We couldn't talk openly about it, so all those sprinklings of wisdom fell on barren ground. It seemed crazy that two intelligent people, who had really loved each other, were unable to talk about what is, probably, the most important thing in life.

'I started to Google for solutions. There is a whole world of solutions out there, but many are superficial or want money to tell you what you already know. I came across the website of two therapists who did something that seemed very different: two of them working intensively with the two of us to get to the bottom of the problems, and guiding us to a better relationship. I sent an email to them late one night, when I was feeling particularly sad and desperate. I was surprised to get an email back almost straight away asking if I wanted to talk then. Neil rang me, and he listened to my story. He sounded very calm and caring. There was something about his voice that was very reassuring. He explained to me how they would be working with us, and sent me an email confirming all the details. He also said he would be very happy to talk to Richard.

'I thought about it all night and wanted to choose the right moment to talk to Richard about it. I knew that if I presented it to him as a fait accompli he would probably run in the other direction. The next evening, when Richard arrived home from work, I cooked a special meal, got the kids out of our hair, poured him a glass of wine and sat down to have dinner, just the two of us. Richard was suspicious.'

'I thought Olivia was going to tell me she was having an affair and wanted me to move out,' Richard interjected, with a smile on his face.

'It felt very awkward,' said Olivia, 'but I told Richard I had loved him and that I knew we were in a really bad place. I assured him I wanted us to work this out and had been searching for solutions. I explained what I had found and told him how it would work.'

'I was very sceptical,' said Richard, 'and when Olivia told me how much it would cost, I almost choked on my fillet mignon. I said I would think about it, but didn't really hold out any hope. I went back behind my wall of resentment – and built another few layers onto it.

'That night, when we got into bed, the space between us spoke volumes, as did the silence. Then Olivia told me that I just didn't care. I exploded, and the argument escalated. We'd had many arguments before, but this was on another level; like a thermo nuclear explosion with all the resentment, blame and bile pouring out. I felt so angry I just needed to get it out physically, and I went down to the kitchen and threw cups, glasses and crockery everywhere. Olivia came down and was shouting at me to grow up and stop. I turned around and saw our three children in the doorway looking astonished. I fell to the floor and broke down. Olivia shepherded them back to bed telling them that everything would be OK, and that we really hadn't liked that crockery anyway.

'She got me back into bed and told me things really had to change. We held each other in a way that we hadn't for years, and we both just cried and cried. We let all the pain flow out until we felt empty and drained.

'I woke up the next morning, looked at Olivia, and knew what I had was too precious to lose. I went downstairs and was amazed to see how a few cups, plates and glasses can become millions of tiny bits spread far and wide. I did my best to clear up, but years later we are still finding some bits – a good reminder of how bad things had got! I left quickly, because I couldn't face the embarrassment of seeing the children.

'I went to work, pretending that everything was OK. But I couldn't concentrate, and mid-morning I went for a walk and phoned the number that Olivia had given me and spoke to Neil. It felt cathartic talking through the previous night, and being listened to and understood. I felt that I wasn't being judged. I also felt that there was a solution out there, if only we were prepared to seize it and work on it. I booked to see them one evening a week later and sent Olivia a text to tell her.'

'I woke up the next morning as if I was trapped in a bad dream,' said Olivia. 'The night played back in slow motion like a horror film. It felt like both of us had crossed a line and there was no going back to how things had been. I got dressed, went downstairs and saw that Richard had done a man-style clear up. I did a bit more sweeping and hoovering, got the children up and made them breakfast. They all looked embarrassed. I told them that their father and I had had a really bad argument, but that we were resolving things and it would be OK. I got them off to school and sat down and cried. I cried for what had happened. I cried for all I had lost in the last twenty years. I cried for all the shattered dreams and hopes. I cried in fear of the future, together or apart. Then my phone bleeped and it was Richard telling me he had booked for us to see Neil next Thursday. My heart leapt in hope that there might be a way forward.

'The Thursday came quickly. We were both very uncertain what would happen, and also really worried that nothing might happen. It felt as though this was our last chance, our final bet, and if it didn't work then we knew we could not go on.

'We had both been sent a long questionnaire to fill out to assess each of our perspectives on where we were, how we had got there, and the outcomes we wanted. It felt good to get all of this out, all of the unexplained past and dreams of the future. It also felt really sad that we had known all of this, and felt despair, but had not been able to do anything about it. We were powerless in the face of our own knowledge.'

Olivia went quiet for a moment, and the waiter, who had respectfully given us some space, took the opportunity of the pause in the conversation to clear our plates and serve us with our main courses and wine.

I wondered what Richard and Olivia would say next.

Chapter 14: The Relationship Paradigm - John

We all raised our glasses, and Rachel proposed a toast to Olivia and Richard for their openness and friendship.

'Do start eating,' said Richard. 'This may take a while!' He took a bite of his grilled fish. 'Thursday evening arrived. We had a drive of over an hour to get to the counsellors and were both very quiet in the car, locked into our own thoughts, hopes and fears. The last part of the journey took us through the New Forest as the evening was drawing in, and seeing the horses and donkeys ambling along the moorland presented a beautiful scene of peace.

'Neil and Maria welcomed us into their consulting room. It felt very calm and safe. One wall was lined with books and there were comfortable chairs to relax in. They were very different, but gave us a sense of confidence that they would help us both.

'We sat down, had some tea and coffee and took some deep breaths. They explained how they worked and what would happen in the first session. They would hear both of our stories of what had happened since we first met, with the understanding that with a couple there are always two perspectives, both of which are likely to be different but also equally right. After hearing both perspectives, they would dig back into our earlier lives to get an understanding of the patterns of behaviour that were set up then. The final part would be about clarifying the outcomes we both wanted, to ensure these were coherent and compatible.

'They also explained the ground rules: they operated a no-blame and no-judgement policy. They wanted to understand how we had got to where we were so that they could help us change and move forward. It was also important that we listened to each other without interruption, and that if one of our recollections was different from the other this was down to perception and not reality.

''The time flew past. It was strange to reconnect across twenty years and relive what I was feeling when I fell in love with Olivia, and the excitement and fun of the first few years. But it was really sad to talk through where we had drifted apart and to hear Olivia's story of the last few years. It was also great to be listened to and understood. We both clarified what we wanted, which was to have a really strong, loving relationship.

'At the end of three-and-a-half hours, I felt exhausted, but also felt that everything that needed to be said had come out, from both of us. I asked Neil and Maria if they thought there was any hope for us, and felt relieved when they both said that, from what they had heard, there was a lot of hope that we could both create a new and good relationship.

'They then summarised what would happen next. They gave us homework to do, so they would have more information, and so we would have the opportunity to learn more and put new ideas into practice. They also explained they were available 24/7 by phone or email if we had any questions or problems. This was very unusual, but gave us reassurance that we were embarked on a difficult journey with excellent guides and support.

'We went away feeling cleansed, and hopeful. On the car journey home we were both reflective and quiet. I was busy thinking through everything Olivia had said, as well as smiling at the forgotten memories of our first meetings. It felt like we had started something we didn't know the ending to, but we both knew it was going to be challenging, fun, scary, exciting, and would let out all sorts of emotions that had been buried for too long.'

Richard paused, drank some wine and ate some more fish. 'How did I do?' he asked Olivia.

'Wonderful, darling. Just how I remember it,' Olivia said, and she bent over and gave him a kiss.

'Thank you. Would you like to summarise the second session

while I finish off my fish?'

'Yes. How is this for you two?' Olivia asked us.

'I'm grateful,' I replied. 'This is fascinating.'

'Me too,' said Rachel. 'This is one hell of a dinner party conversation.'

'Well, just wait till we get to the sex!' said Richard with a chuckle.

Olivia blushed a little, but laughed too.

'A week later we met for the second session,' she continued. 'We had been given a lot of homework to do, some of which seemed a bit strange, but Neil and Maria went through this, explained what it meant and highlighted the fact that our communication patterns had been very poor. It was as if we had both been missing the target and creating resentment on both sides. They then explained what they called The Relationship Paradigm.

'Relationships have five separate elements to them. These are interlocked. If they grow together they are much stronger, and if one is absent or weak then the relationship is less strong or resilient. The first element is Communication, the second is Connection, the third is Commitment, the fourth is Fun, and the last one is Growth. Surrounding all of these is Trust. If trust is complete, then it is like a clear blue sky. If trust is beginning to be doubted, then it is as if big grey storm clouds appear and they impact on all the other elements. What I loved about this model was that it was so simple and made such perfect sense.

'They asked us to calibrate where we each were on these elements, writing the word and a score out of ten on each card and putting it where it needed to be. I was puzzled, and asked for clarification, and Neil repeated the instruction.

'We did this and laid out the cards on the floor in different patterns. I was so shocked by my scores, and Richard's, that I can still remember them! I scored four for communication, three for connection, eight for commitment, two for fun, two for growth and nine for trust. Richard gave a score of five for communication, four for connection, nine for commitment, six for fun, four for growth and six for trust.

'How on earth did we get there? The only hope was that we were both really committed to trying to make it work. We knew to carry on as we were would be too painful, and to split up would be a waste of all our years invested in the relationship and would really damage the children. It was then that we knew we needed to do this, and said we were ready to hear about the first element of the paradigm.'

THE RELATIONSHIP PARADIGM

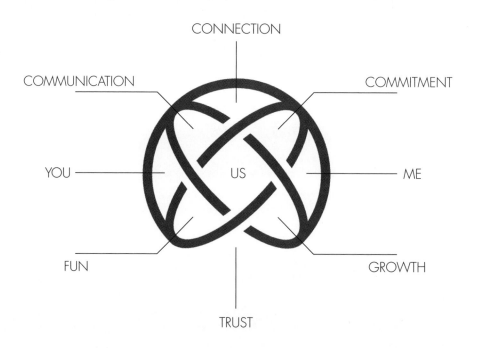

The Relationship Paradigm is a representation of the elements that I believe are fundamental to a great relationship between two people.

The model opposite shows the way in which the elements of Communication, Connection, Commitment, Fun and Growth create a connection between the 'You' and 'Me' to create an 'Us'

The element of Trust is the foundation of this model. Without trust the whole model becomes unstable and dissipates.

You cannot not communicate.

– Reg Percival

Chapter 15: The First Element

COMMUNICATION

'The rest of the session focused on the first element of communication,' Olivia continued. 'They explained the patterns we had got trapped in, and the subtle changes that would make a significant difference. They described communication as being much more than words. It is also about being able to express your feelings to each other, subtly or directly, without fear of being judged; about knowing that your partner will listen to you and, even if they don't agree, will understand. It is also about being able to talk through differences of opinion, knowing you may not be able to agree, but that the difference will be accepted and will not pollute the rest of your relationship.

'We left that session with surprising insights into what we had been getting wrong for so long, and an understanding of the negative impact that had been having on our relationship. We were given some exercises to do before the next session. We did some of these face to face, and some by email, phone and text. Richard had an important overseas conference to go to, so our next session was three weeks later.'

Olivia turned to Richard, held out her hand and said, 'Do you remember how we had been getting it so wrong?'

Richard caressed her hand. 'Yes, we both thought we were doing the right thing and the other was at fault. Two messages that surprised me, but made perfect sense, were: "Treat others how they want to be treated," not, as I had been told by my parents, treat others as you would like to be treated, and, "The meaning of any communication is the message that is received."'

'Yes, there were many other things we were doing, with good intentions, but they were just wrong for each other,' Olivia interjected. 'So, we left that session having learned a huge amount, and feeling excited about what might happen next.'

The waiter saw that we had finished our main courses and brought some menus for the desserts. We ordered, and both red and white wine were brought to the table.

I turned to Richard and asked, 'Do you do this every holiday?'

Richard smiled and said, 'No, John, don't worry! We feel immensely privileged to have had the opportunity to create a new and wonderful relationship with each other, and are very happy to share what we learned with others. But normally they don't get our whole life story! Generally, we just say we know someone who might be able to help. What has made it different this time is us being here and celebrating the tenth anniversary of our new start, and having the time and space to talk with two willing listeners. It is great for us to be able to remind ourselves of the journey we have been on.'

'Another gem I remember,' Olivia said, 'was about "changing your world one conversation at a time." Words can be so powerful, and to be able to get them out into the air and see the impact they are having on others is a real joy.'

Desserts appeared and we quietly started eating.

'I'm really grateful to you both,' Rachel said. 'You've given us so much to think about, and I'm sure it will really help us.'

'All we ask is that you tell us when you've heard enough!'

Richard laughed.

Rachel smiled. 'Can you tell us about the further sessions, and highlights of the last ten years?'

Olivia giggled and said, 'Well, the last ten years have been full of blessings and highlights. There have also been difficulties with family and work, but we have been able to work together as a team to get through the downs. Our relationship has blossomed but, like a garden, it requires time and attention to nurture and help it grow in the right way. The highlights would take rather too much time to go through. We would rather you create your own highlights, for your future. So shall we give you a quick run through of the other sessions, just to help you understand the other elements of the paradigm?'

'Yes, please!' Rachel and I said together, and looked at each other and smiled in surprise.

'Well, stop me, Richard, if I go off track!' Olivia said.

The meeting of two personalities is like the contact of two chemical substances. If there is any reaction, both are transformed.

– Carl Jung

Chapter 16: The Second Element

CONNECTION

'Connection is about big things and small things,' Olivia said. 'It's about looks, touches, being in the same space, conversations and even sex. It's about making sure there are times in every day where you are there for each other and fully present. Life will always get in the way, but you have to find ways around any road blocks. The counsellors talked about something called Bids for Connection and the fact that for every bid that is turned away from or against there need to be at least five bids that are turned towards.'

Olivia stopped, took a sip of her wine, looked at Rachel and said, 'Is this making any sense to you? It sounds as if I have suddenly become an expert on relationships!'

'It is making some sense, and my mind is whirling around thinking of all the things we are getting wrong. What do you think, John?'

'Hmm...' John pondered, obviously deep in thought.

Olivia put down her glass and said, 'What is really important is to talk to each other about the sorts of connection you both want, so you can understand the other's needs. Even about sex.' She blushed a little and patted Richard's leg. 'Sex is a really important form of connection that many people regard as embarrassing to talk about.'

'I remember symbols of connection including things like what happens when you part in the morning and reconnect every night, answering the phone when they call, and calling back as soon as you can if you can't, and small, surprise gifts that meant "I was thinking of you", as well as saying nice affirmative things to each other, and making special time to just be. I think that's about it. Richard and I have our "annual review" when we are away on holiday, and share what is going well and what we could do even better in ways of connecting. We are still giving each other gold stars! Over to you, Richard, for the next part – after you've got us another bottle of wine. All this talk of sex is making me thirsty!'

*Relationships are the thing that
either hinge us, or break us.*

– Kimberley L Miller

Chapter 17: The Third Element

COMMITMENT

'So,' Richard said, 'the third element is commitment, which involves you both being clear about what you want from life, for yourself and from the relationship. You both need to be heading in the same direction.

'A metaphor that you might like, Rachel, is imagine you both get into a yacht on the day you get married and head out to sea. If you're not clear about where you each want to go as a destination, and the roles you both want to take, there will be confusion. There will be storms, tides, calms and all sorts of things that will make the journey difficult, and if you haven't decided what your roles are then dealing with the difficulties will be much harder.

'The other important thing is to realise that a great relationship is the best thing on earth, but it is hard work and life gets in the way. My work meant I had forgotten to keep our relationship alive and that was seen by Olivia as a lack of commitment. It fell to the bottom of the queue and our boat was left drifting with both of us wanting to jump into separate life rafts.

'We regularly check in with each other now to make sure we are sailing the same course, and have the desire to fight our way through storms as well as to enjoy the sunshine and sunsets. If only we had started to do that years ago, when Ami was born, we could have had even more fun.'

Richard raised his glass. 'To Olivia,' he said. 'Thank you for staying in the boat with me. The last ten years have been wonderful. Over to you, my darling, to talk about fun. That's the part I love!'

The most wasted of days is one without laughter.

– E E Cummings

Chapter 18: The Fourth Element

FUN

'I hope you don't think we're one of those irritatingly perfect couples with a house out of Country Life, children from Tatler and a story from Hello magazine!' Olivia laughed. 'My kitchen looks like a bomb has gone off, the vacuum cleaner gave up on the dog hairs months ago, and I fart in bed. Our children are lovely, though!'

All three laughed with her when she said this, and we looked at each other with raised eyebrows: Olivia farts in bed!

'One of the questions we were asked when we started our counselling was, When did you last have fun? I had to think and think, and felt really embarrassed to say that it was a long time ago. We used to have such fun together when we first met, but children and work and stuff just distracted us from one of the most important things in life: to enjoy life.

'It was shocking to realise that fun had simply disappeared from our agendas, and it seemed a bit fake planning to have fun, but a few pillow fights and jelly-throwing competitions later and we really got into it. The children gave us some very strange looks and muttered a lot, but when we explained the importance to them and involved them, they started to let their hair down, too.

'It proved to be a great antidote to the stress of everyday life and brought a whole sense of lightness into our lives together. We'll spare you a demonstration! If I asked you both when did you last have fun together, what would you answer?'

'Until we came here, it was a long time ago,' Rachel admitted. 'Maybe it was about two years ago at our neighbours' New Year's Eve party, when we all got very drunk and did the hokey cokey around the block!'

'That doesn't count,' Olivia smiled. 'It has to be just the two of you.'

'Oh, in that case I can't really remember. Can you, John?'

'Erm... No, I can't. Thinking about it makes me realise just how serious and dull we've become.'

'Never mind,' Richard said. 'A future of fun beckons. Just unleash the child within, as they know all the answers!'

Be the change you want to see.

– Ghandi

Chapter 19: The Fifth Element

GROWTH

'We are almost at the end of describing the paradigm,' Richard said. 'Growth is the next area, as without it a relationship stagnates and a couple will drift apart, like we did. I assumed that the love we had when we first met thirty years ago would be rock-solid and triumph over adversity. What I hadn't realised is it's a living thing that needs to be nourished and taken care of. When there are also things like children, work, money and stuff to be dealt with, they can become the priority, and growth of the relationship dissipates. I just assumed that we were growing, when actually we were fading.

'So, for the first time in our lives, we sat down and talked through what we wanted out of life, what was really important to us, and how we could work together to achieve that. We now have a big dream board on our kitchen wall and regularly update it and talk through how we're doing.

'We also talk about our why: why we were doing what we were doing in life rather than focusing on our what or how. That really transforms the depth and quality of our thinking.

'Growth as individuals is also hugely important. A great relationship needs two fulfilled individuals and an "us" that is also fulfilled. Couples should be interdependent and not fused. I decided to take up a new hobby, flying; and Olivia did an Open University degree in psychology. That helped us both get out of the rut we had slumped into.

'OK, that's my bit, I think!' he then laughed. 'What about some coffee and chocolates?' He waved to the waiter, who came and cleared the plates and handed out the coffee menu. 'I shouldn't really have anything,' he then said, 'but this is our last night and the locally grown coffee is amazing. I think we need brandies, too, to go with the coffee!'

We all ordered and coffee, brandy and chocolates were served.

John took a sip and turned to Richard. 'This all makes perfect sense so far, but how does trust feature in this?' he asked.

'Over to you, Olivia,' Richard smiled.

Trust starts with truth, and ends with truth.

– Santosh Kalwar

Chapter 20

TRUST

Olivia sipped her coffee and helped herself to one of the chocolates. 'Wow, that is lovely,' she said, licking her lips. 'Trust was the last part of the paradigm we focused on. Trust was not a big issue for us, because there had not been an actual affair, just Richard's suspicions based on the fact we had drifted apart. Trust is like a sea mist that sweeps in and makes it hard to see, and reality becomes a dark place difficult to escape from. Rebuilding trust requires absolute clarity over the direction you are going in, and total openness about what you are doing, and who you are talking to and seeing. It means opening up your phones and emails to each other so that there is no scope for suspicion.

'I had no reason to mistrust Richard, but when your relationship is in a bad place the imagination can go wild. When we started talking about our feelings and perspectives, the reasons for where we had got to became very understandable.

'So, ten years ago, it felt like the sea mist cleared, the sun shone and we could start to work together on the new relationship we both wanted and to leave our past problems behind. The work continues, and we have continued to learn and grow. The last ten years have been the best of our lives and I feel really fortunate.' She sent Richard a look of complete love and admiration. 'We worked hard, and still work hard, and deserve to be happy,' she concluded.

There was a pause, and then Rachel said, 'Thank you so much. It's incredible that you have both been so open with us. If there was one thing you would recommend, what would it be?'

Richard and Olivia said in unison: 'Go and see Neil and Maria.'

'We couldn't have done it without them,' Richard added. He looked warmly at us both. 'It's been a lovely evening, but we need to get to bed. We have an early start for an island boat tour tomorrow before we fly back in the evening. Do call us when you get back. It would be good to meet up for dinner.'

Rachel and Olivia exchanged email addresses and phone numbers, and we said our goodbyes, once more expressing thanks for such a wonderful evening.

Chapter 21: Tipping Point - John

Rachel and I held hands on the way back to our room and got into bed together. Rachel started to cry. 'What's wrong?' I asked.

'I will miss them,' she said. 'They've been so generous with their time and have been very open with us. It feels like they've given us an amazing gift, but I'm not sure if we know what to do with it.'

'I don't know what to say. I think they've given us lots of ideas; all we have to do is choose which are the best ones and put them into practice.'

But in between the sobs Rachel said, 'I don't think you really get this. I feel we've been given a glimpse of something wonderful, but it could turn out to be a mirage.'

'Let's talk about this tomorrow,' I said. 'I deal with complex legal agreements every day. In comparison, this seems pretty simple.' I turned my back on Rachel.

I heard Rachel swear, and then she got up and went out onto the balcony and stood looking out at the pool. I could hear the gentle sounds of the waves in the distance. The glimmer of hope that had been created in the last few days felt like it was draining away. I knew this was incredibly important for us both, and would need real commitment and hard work, but I just wasn't sure contacting Neil and Maria was the right thing to do. I was pretty sure Rachel was going to shout at me when she came back into the room; but instead she went to the fridge and took out a bottle of rosé and a packet of nuts. She went back out to the balcony and, as I fell asleep, I guessed she would now get drunk.

I woke up to the warmth from the sun and the sound of some dreadful rock music coming through the tinny speakers on

Rachel's phone. Where was she? She wasn't in bed? I had a sense of foreboding. The night had seemed so full of promise but had ended in tears. Rachel and I seemed to have read the same book but drawn very different conclusions from it.

Rachel later told me she had woken up on the balcony, shivering with cold and with a deep throbbing at the front of her head. She said she came back into the room, where I was noisily snoring, and prodded me, but that I'd just grunted and started snoring in a different key, so she'd gone back out onto the balcony. I sat up and looked out: she was in the bathtub drinking coffee and eating biscuits.

I needed some coffee, too, and some food. I got out of bed and walked out onto the balcony. Rachel looked up at me with a frown on her face. 'Are you OK?' I asked.

'What a stupid question!' she snapped back. 'Don't you ever listen?'

'What have I done wrong?'

Rachel stared at me. 'If you don't know now, you never will!'

I indicated the empty bottle of rosé, and said, 'Ah, I see. Let's go and have some breakfast and you can sober up.'

She threw a bottle of shampoo at me and shouted, 'You condescending prick! Get lost!'

I decided it would be better to withdraw before we got trapped in a shouting match, and said, 'I'm going for breakfast. Shall I see you down there?'

Rachel glared at me. 'Do you ever learn?'

I turned and went back into the room, put on a t-shirt and shorts and headed down to breakfast.

Feeling puzzled and a bit hurt I really tucked in to the buffet: an omelette, a plate full of hash browns, several coffees, too many pain au raisins to count and, before I became too tempted by the pancakes and syrup, a large plate of fresh fruit – the perfect antidote to all the carbs.

I reflected on everything that had happened since we had

arrived; the dream holiday turning sour so quickly; the fleeting moments where Rachel seemed to have sorted herself out and then changed back to her old self. And then the intervention of Olivia and Richard. Nice people, and an interesting story, but Rachel appeared to have become mesmerised by them and was taking everything they said and wanting to apply it all, carte blanche, to our lives.

I really didn't understand why she'd got so upset last night, and so angry this morning, and what I needed to do to calm her down and help her realise that if only she changed and became more reasonable, then things would be OK.

I felt a hand on my shoulder. Rachel sat down opposite me and looked me in the eyes. 'I'm sorry I shouted at you, but I felt so frustrated at you ignoring the reality of this and trying to brush things under the carpet. For the first time I've seen an answer for us, that makes sense, and I'm worried you don't get it.'

'OK, then let's talk about it, but not here,' I said, worried that we might be overheard.

'When, then?'

'How about tonight? In the meantime, can we just relax? I feel like I've been under the spotlight for several days and need to chill.'

'OK,' Rachel said. 'Have you left any croissants?' she then asked.

'Just a few,' I said. 'But don't eat too many.'

'Hmm...' she responded, looking at my stomach.

Breakfast continued in silence. When Rachel had finished, I asked her what she wanted to do today.

'I don't know,' she said. 'What do you want to do?'

'I'm not sure.' I felt frustrated. How was I supposed to guess what she wanted to do?

'Why don't we go snorkelling this morning?' she suggested. 'If you can still float after that breakfast.'

'Alright,' I said, feeling unenthusiastic but wanting to keep the peace.

We went down to the beach to pick up the dive boat. Along with the frustration, I admit I also felt despondent, particularly when we joined up with all the other couples who were smiling, laughing, touching, and looked so much in love. I too felt I had glimpsed something great in the last couple of days, only to have it blown away as if it was a mirage. I just didn't know what to do with it, if I'm honest.

We sat down next to each other on the deck as the boat headed out. Rachel reached out and stroked my arm. 'Let's enjoy the day,' she said, and kissed me on the lips.

I felt a warm glow spreading upwards and blushed. I looked around to see if anyone was watching, but they were all wrapped up in themselves. I smiled and said, 'OK.'

The snorkelling was pleasant, but the water was a bit cloudy so I only saw a few interesting fish. Rachel quickly headed off on her own and I felt a bit ignored.

When we got back, we had a quiet lunch, and then Rachel went off sailing while I lay and read and had a few beers. She appeared later on looking annoyingly energised and suggested we went and sat at the pool bar. I went along and had a few quiet cocktails, while she started chatting to a Swedish couple. I didn't feel like talking and was getting increasingly annoyed that she seemed to be so happy and obviously didn't need me. Who was paying for this holiday, after all?

I withdrew even further, and felt the resentment building up to how it had been before we came out here. I sat there nursing my drink, looking down, and heard Rachel saying goodbye to the other couple. 'Come on, Mr Grumpy,' she then said, and grabbed my arm. 'Come with me. I've got something to show you.'

'What?' I asked.

'I'm not saying, it's a secret,' she whispered in my ear. 'It's in our room.'

'Do I have to?'

'You will like it,' she said as she squeezed my thigh.

'OK...'

I opened the door, feeling confused. Rachel pushed me into the room and told me to close my eyes and not speak. I felt her put a sleep mask on my face and started to ask what on earth she was doing.

'Shhh...' she said. 'You've been a very naughty boy and it's time I punished you.'

I started to protest, but she hit me firmly on the backside and said, 'I'm in charge now. You have to do as I tell you.'

My brain was protesting, but my penis started to get interested. I decided this was weird, and different, but could be fun.

Rachel saw my hardness and rubbed against me. 'That's better,' she said. 'You respond well to some punishment. I'm going to undress you now, so that I can see you properly.'

She pulled off my t-shirt and swimming shorts and pushed me onto the bed, where she pulled my legs out straight and started to tie my left ankle to the bedpost and then the right. Again I started to protest, but decided to relax and go with the flow – with a very different and unexpected Rachel. And then both of my wrists got pulled out and tied up. I lay there squirming, feeling nervous, and also very excited.

I heard Rachel taking her clothes off and rubbing something onto her body. I then felt the warmth of her skin as she slid on top of me and rubbed her breasts over my chest and down to my genitals. I started to get really hard and heard her whisper, 'Yes, you need some real punishment,' as she took my penis into her mouth and started to nibble and suck.

I realised one of my childhood fantasies was coming true, but without warning was transported over thirty years back to my school bedroom, remembering the feeling of embarrassment as some boys walked into my room, saw me masturbating and pointed at me, laughing, and called me Mini Willy. And guess what... Mini Willy suddenly became Mini Willy again – really Mini Willy. Rachel tried valiantly, but the odds were against, and she slid off to lie next to me. She stroked my chest and said, 'I'm sorry, was it too much for you?'

Much to my surprise, I started to cry, and the tears flooded down my cheeks as I let out all those years of ridicule.

'What's wrong?' she asked. 'Please tell me?'

'It's a long story,' I said. 'But thank you for trying.'

'When you are ready.' Rachel got off the bed and started to untie me. She then got dressed and left the room.

How could she leave me like this? Feeling angry, hurt and rejected I got dressed, went down to the pool bar and started drinking cocktails – and got very, very drunk.

Rachel eventually joined me. She took the glass out of my hand and I heard her say, 'Maybe that's enough. We need to talk. Let's go and find somewhere quiet.'

'Probably not a good idea,' I mumbled. 'I'm feeling a bit ill.'

She took hold of my wrist and gently pulled me away from the bar. I pulled against her, but she was stronger, so I stopped fighting and allowed her to lead me away to a quiet corner in the shade.

'Lie down there,' she said, and I fell backwards on to the sunbed.

She sat down and held my arm. 'I'm sorry if I did something wrong back there,' she said. 'I was way outside my comfort zone, but wanted to try and heal the rift between us by doing something different. I don't know what was happening for you, but I feel incredibly embarrassed and hurt. I'm not prepared to allow things to wallow along as they are, and I need you to decide what the hell it is you want.'

I found it hard to get my thoughts together, and my mouth was struggling to enunciate. 'It brought back horrible memories for me, from when I was younger, and made me feel very stupid,' I said. 'I'm feeling trapped and I don't know what to do.'

'Well, maybe it's make-your-mind-up time. We have a few hours to dinner. I suggest you sober up and we will talk later.'

Shit, I thought, as the effects of the sunshine and the cocktails eased me into sleep.

I woke up a few hours later with a thumping headache. The sun had set and I stumbled back to the room and knocked on the door.

Eventually Rachel answered with a towel around her.

'Oh,' she said. 'How are you? You look terrible.'

'Not good. Maybe I had a bit too much to drink.'

'Probably,' she said. 'You often do. Come in, have a shower and get dressed. We need to get some food and talk this evening.'

'Do we have to? I'm feeling awful.'

'Yes,' she said, fixing me with a hard stare. 'I'm not prepared to wait any longer. Have a coffee and some water and make yourself look decent. I'm going back to my bath.'

'Alright,' I said, feeling I was being controlled, and headed for the shower.

A long hot shower, a cold shower, two cups of coffee and a jug of water later I felt a bit better, but wet inside and out. I got dressed, ready for my meeting with the headmistress, and felt anxious and very small. Mini Willy had all but disappeared.

Rachel led the way to dinner. She had booked a quiet corner in the very upmarket Italian restaurant with candles and linen napkins. All the other couples there looked very romantic. I was being outgunned by a very stern-looking Rachel.

After ordering food and Rachel telling the waiter that we were definitely not having any wine, she looked me in the eye and started talking. She told me how angry she was that we had got to where we were – many years invested in what had become a failed relationship – and that I was avoiding taking any responsibility and ignoring opportunities to resolve it. She said, 'You have a choice: try and fix this, or I want you to move out as soon as we get back. I'm not putting up with this anymore.'

My heart sank. I felt trapped; I felt cornered; and I felt sick. I got up and rushed to the men's room, and barely made it into the cubicle before I threw up into the bowl. I retched and retched until I felt my insides were becoming outsides. I flushed the toilet, washed my face and walked back to the table. The table was empty. Rachel was no longer there.

I headed outside. I saw someone who looked like Rachel walking towards the beach. I followed and caught up with her by the edge of the sea. When she heard me behind, she whirled round and shouted at me, 'Where the hell did you run away to? I was so embarrassed being left on my own!'

'I had to go to the toilet and throw up. I felt ill and trapped, and now I feel there is no hope.'

Rachel glared at me. 'I've been supportive and gentle. I tried really hard to reconnect this afternoon, and all you do is keep putting things off. I told you what I need. Are you man enough to make a decision, or will I have to?'

'OK,' I said, 'please let me think about it; it all feels too much at the moment.'

'For fuck's sake! You've had eighteen years! How fucking long do you need?'

'Look, I want this to work, but it needs to be a decision where I understand what my part is and what I need to do. You've been swept along by the Olivia and Richard love story; you've jumped to conclusions; and you just don't seem to realise that I need time to think about these things!'

Rachel walked to the water's edge, picked up some stones and started throwing them into the sea. She then sat down on the sand and started to sob. I could see her shoulders heaving and the sound of her crying. I went up and sat beside her on the warm, but slightly damp sand.

'I know you are angry. Let's talk when you have calmed down,' I said.

Rachel turned to me and punched me in the chest, hard. 'One out of ten for communication!' she yelled. 'I'm not angry! I'm frustrated, hurt and despairing! And don't patronise me. We need to talk now, not at some vague time in the future when you feel like it.'

I felt totally out of my depth and even more cornered. I just wished everything would go away and I could crawl into a hole in the sand where no one could find me. I took a really deep breath and tried to think what it was I really wanted out of life. All my dreams of family, a lovely house and senior partnership at work seemed to disappear, and all I was left with was bills to pay, a family that hated me, and no fun. What was the point?

I reached out and tried to put my arm around Rachel's shoulder, but felt her shudder and throw me off. 'Look,' I said, 'I promise I will talk and we will work out a solution to this. Let's do it tomorrow, and then we can spend the remaining time enjoying being here. Now isn't the time. My head and body are all over the place and I need to sober up.'

'OK,' Rachel said. 'Tomorrow at ten, or else.'

'Are you going to bed now?'

'No. I'm going to sit here and watch the stars.'

I walked back to the room feeling so alone, got into bed and fell asleep.

Chapter 22: Tipping Point - Rachel

When Olivia and Richard left it felt sad waving goodbye to two people who had given us so much; but I also felt full of hope that they had shown us an incredible glimpse of future possibilities. All that John and I needed to do was to put all this learning into action.

But when I was left alone with John it felt like the bright hope dissipated with his refusal to commit. I felt there was no point talking to him as he wasn't really listening; my words were falling on barren soil, as they had for too many years.

My only escape that night was to get very pissed and fall into bed next to a man I believe honestly wanted to be somewhere else. When I went back into the bedroom, though, John was snoring so loudly that I had to go back onto the balcony.

Waking up in the morning, cold and with a banging head, I felt like I had gone, in a day, from a wonderful dream to a nightmare from which there was no escape. I had been shown that our marriage was hopeless, and that my husband was incapable of helping me to change it. I got into the bath, like a return to the womb, hoping for a rebirth. The view was lovely, and I was beginning to calm down when the John I really hate appeared and spoilt it all. He then went off to pig out on breakfast, leaving me to stew. I calmed down as I looked at the beautiful clear blue sea, though, and smelt the flowers. It was crazy, being unhappy in such a beautiful place. I thought it would be good to get John somewhere different later, away from the bar, where he could feel the beauty of this place.

I had to bite my tongue as I walked into the restaurant and saw him covered in crumbs from all the croissants he had obviously been eating. A sinking feeling hit me in the pit of my stomach:

who was this man who I had been with for eighteen years and now didn't recognise or even like? It felt like I was poised on the edge of a canyon, and I had to leap to the other side before I lost my courage or I would be trapped in this place for ever.

I breathed deeply, focused on the future that I wanted for us – a future of love, connection and growth – and decided I would have to dig deep into my resources and see if I could get John to leap over the canyon with me. But first I needed to get him away from the never-ending breakfast and the state of self-pity he seemed to be in. I also decided I would almost need to seduce him to get him to do the things I wanted to naturally do with my partner of the future – him.

John reluctantly came snorkelling with me. He wasn't great company to start with, which was probably not helped by his hangover. I gave him a kiss on the boat, which seemed to cheer him up, but his response felt rather passive. The sea was fairly clear and we went over the side of the boat. John has never been a great swimmer, and I got frustrated that he didn't want to go deeper or further. I saw a big school of fish going past and pointed them out to him, and headed off in pursuit; but he didn't follow, so I left him to it. There were many other fish in the sea...

When we got back, lunch was rather monosyllabic, and I was desperate to get some sort of reaction. Attempts at conversation went nowhere, however.

I decided I needed to get away for a while to restore my energy and went sailing for a couple of hours. I had a sense of freedom and exhilaration, surging through the waves. Feeling at one with nature and being responsible for everything I touched was really liberating. I wondered what life would be like on my own, without John. It could be fun, but the three children meant we would be tied together for many years, and there was no real escape.

I came back to the beach, handed the dinghy back to one of the boat boys, and decided to take the bull by the horns – or even John by his manhood.

I had read many books on relationships, and some on the subject of reenergising a flatlining sex life. Our sex had become utterly predictable and lacked any style. It was hard to get aroused by John's beery breath and paunch when he climbed on top, pumped away and then, fulfilled, climbed off me thinking he had done me a great favour. A few days ago he had really surprised me when he went down on me in the morning, so I thought I would try something new and inventive for him.

I decided to entice him back to our room and see if I could work some magic. It was a disaster. I had got there full of hope, and way out of my comfort zone. At first it seemed exciting, and John seemed really turned on; but trying to give head to a man with a rapidly shrinking penis who then bursts into tears is the most humiliating thing I have ever done. It made me think he clearly didn't fancy me anymore, and I started wondering who he was having an affair with, and what was behind all those late nights at work?

I left him in our bedroom, full of anger and shame, and went for a long walk along the beach. I got back after a couple of hours and found John hanging off a stool at the bar, obviously a few cocktails down. I took him to a quiet corner and tried to talk to him but got no sense, so left him to sleep on the sunbed.

I went back to the room to sort myself out, and to do what I had hoped John would do for me earlier. I then had a long bath and allowed the stress and negativity to wash away. I wasn't ready to give up yet; a great relationship with John was still a possibility, but a diminishing one.

I booked a table at the Italian restaurant. *This is the last throw of the dice*, I thought. With what we had learned this holiday, if John was not able to up his game then there was no hope at all.

A beautiful restaurant, soft lighting, a pianist playing gently in the background and the smell of delicious food cooking...this would be a wonderfully romantic place to bring the man I loved. Sadly, it was John facing me, hungover, sweating, and just wanting another drink. The dam holding back all my years of anger and frustration burst and I laid into him. He shrivelled in his chair when I told him I'd had enough and needed some commitment from him; he shrivelled even more when I said he needed to take responsibility, and grab this opportunity, and that if he didn't we would split up when we got home. He said he needed time to think and rushed off to the toilet. I waited for ages, but with no sign of him stormed out of the restaurant and headed down to the beach to calm down.

I kicked off my shoes and paddled in the sea, feeling the sand between my toes. The water helped my anger fade, but I looked up at the stars in the clear night sky and felt alone, insignificant and vulnerable. I turned round and headed back to the restaurant to see if I could find John. Halfway there I thought, *Why am I doing this*? and went back to the purity of the beach and the water. I heard a sound behind me, and John sat down next to me and tried to put his arm around me. I could smell the alcohol and vomit on his breath. I felt repulsed and shrugged him off. I whirled round and shouted, 'Where the hell did you go? I was so embarrassed!'

His answers made no sense to me, and sounded like he was avoiding taking any responsibility and delaying any decisions. I went down to the water's edge and picked up some pebbles. I threw one in the water for every year of misery in our relationship. I threw one for everything about John that I didn't like. I threw one for everything about myself that I wanted to change, and by the time I'd finished the sea was full of pebbles, so I sat on the beach and sobbed. Vomit-breath came and sat beside me and once again, tried to put his arm around me; and once again he put off talking about the most important thing in my life.

I gave him an ultimatum that by ten in the morning we would talk. He agreed and lurched off to bed, leaving me alone on the beach looking at the stars and wondering, not just if there was life out there, but whether there was any life in him.

Chapter 23: A Step Forward - Rachel

Fortunately, our room had a sofa, and not wanting to sleep on the balcony again I was hoping to get some sleep a few feet away from a smelly, snoring man. Thoughts were whirling through my mind, though, blanking out hope of sleep. I felt good that at least we had a time scheduled for our conversation; but angry it all seemed to be down to me to make it happen.

Eventually I drifted off, but not before I had seriously considered using a spare pillow as a lasting solution to John's snoring. My night was short and full of scary dreams.

I was standing in the dark. The wind was blowing and the ground under my bare feet felt like sharp shingle. I could not see much, but I sensed I was at the edge of a steep drop. I could hear water flowing fast, way down in the depths. I took a nervous step forward, and heard a stone tumbling over the edge and, after a long, long time, a faint splash below. I lurched backwards and stopped: there was something immovable behind me. I reached out with my hands and explored with my fingers. It felt like cold stone, all the way to the left, the right and above. I started to shiver. I was cold and frightened. *How did I get here?* I wondered. I was stuck and couldn't see, but I had to move, so I inched my way to the left, turned my body around so I was facing the rock and moved slowly. My hand touched something that felt slimy, and it moved. I recoiled, and lurched backwards, and felt myself falling through the air. I screamed and tried desperately to reach out and hold onto something to stop me from falling, but there was nothing there, just the cold air, and I carried on hurtling downwards until, with a huge splash, I hit cold water. I sank under the water; it filled my lungs and I started to cough and flailed my arms to try and swim. But I kept going down into the cold depths, and then my thoughts, my awareness, faded like the sound of an old-fashioned valve radio being turned off and the sound faded away into nothingness.

I awoke into bright sunlight, my screams echoing off the ceiling and my arms wildly waving. I sat up and realised where I was, looked around and saw John in the bed, fast asleep and totally oblivious. I didn't know whether to shout, scream or cry. I decided that life was too short; I had survived the maelstrom and was alive. I started to laugh, quietly at first, and then the hysteria grabbed hold of me and it got louder and louder. My chest was heaving, trying to get air into my lungs. John woke up, and looked at me with utter confusion.

I carried on laughing. I couldn't stop. And it felt totally insane. I was laughing so much that my body spasmed off the bed and I banged my head on the floor, but still I couldn't stop laughing. It was like the dam had broken and all the years of pain, anger and frustration were being washed away by this onslaught of laughter. After what seemed like hours, my breathing started to recover and I crawled back onto the sofa and lay there gasping.

'Are you OK?' John finally asked. 'It was a real shock to be woken up by that.'

'I'm good,' I said. 'I haven't had a laugh like that for a long, long time. You should try it.'

'I can't,' he said. 'I've got an appointment with my wife in twenty minutes and I can't be late. Have you seen her?'

'No,' I said. 'What does she look like?'

'I'm not sure,' he said. 'But she normally looks a bit sad.'

'That's a real shame. What would cheer her up, do you know?'

'Probably if I turned up on time and did what I was told,' he said.

'Oh, is she rather bossy, then?'

'She never used to be, but she's changed a lot since coming out here.'

'What are you meeting about?' I asked.

'She said we have to talk about the future or we are over.'

'Gosh, that is serious. It sounds like your future is at stake. Better get dressed and make yourself look smart for your bossy wife.'

I went and had a quick shower, threw on some clothes, grabbed a notebook, pen and hat, and headed out of the door to the restaurant.

Five minutes later John appeared at the entrance looking a bit worried and glancing at his watch. He looked around, saw me and walked over to the table.

'Good morning,' I said. 'My name is Rachel and I'm here to represent your wife. Have a seat.' As John sat down I pulled out my pad and pen and said, 'OK, now John, we need to talk about the future, and Rachel wants to know what you are going to do to make it a better future.'

John gulped and took an envelope out of his pocket and handed it to me. I looked at the thick, handmade paper and lifted the flap. Inside was a card with a hand-drawn picture of the sun rising over a calm blue sea. I opened the card, read the words and started to cry: *Rachel, I'm so sorry I have let you down all these years. I want to make it right for you, for us, and our children. Please can we start again? Your husband John.*

'Thank you,' I said. 'I'll give this to Rachel.' I stood up and left the restaurant, took a deep breath and went back in. I bent down behind John and whispered in his ear, 'I love you.' I stroked the top of his head, and sat down opposite him and took his hands in mine. 'Thank you. The future starts here. What is next?'

John squeezed my hands and said, 'Well, when we get back maybe we need some expert help to work through our plans. In the remaining few days, can we just relax and enjoy time together?'

'Does that mean you don't want to talk about our stuff until we get back?'

'Yes, I think that will be better,' he said. 'Otherwise we are in danger of having an argument with no one to help us.'

'Alright,' I said. 'As long as you promise we will start talking when we get back.'

'Maybe you could teach me to laugh?' he said.

'OK, you're on,' I said.

Our final days in Grenada were good. We relaxed, ate, drank, enjoyed being with each other; and I also enjoyed time on my own, sailing, swimming and sunbathing. John did try and get me interested in sex, and we made love a few times, but I wasn't really in the mood and wanted to sleep.

The evening of departure came quickly and I left with mixed feelings: sad to leave such a lovely place; excited about the possibilities the conversations with Olivia and Richard had opened up; and very scared about the uncertainty this had created. Would John and I stay together, or would we split up?

Chapter 24: The Ultimatum - John

I woke up with a start. Someone was laughing hysterically in the room. I felt really groggy and remembered the last night had been pretty disastrous.

I looked through my haze and saw that Rachel was laughing uncontrollably. What on earth had got into her? I had never seen her like this before! Maybe she had been on the ganja?

Then I remembered with a real dread that she had demanded we would talk at ten this morning, or else. There was no escape. She had been very aggressive. Then she scared me and started talking as if she was a third person! She must have had something weird after I went off to bed. I thought it better to humour her, and played along.

She gave me a kiss, but I could see that sex was not on the agenda.

After Rachel had showered, I had a cold shower to wake myself up. I wasn't sure how to cope with the ten o'clock meeting in the headmistress's office. I wondered if I could avoid talking about all the deep stuff, and had a rummage in the table drawer for some paper to write down my thoughts.

I found some really nice cards. What could I say? What did I need to say? What did I really feel?

I picked up a pen and started writing. I found it surprisingly difficult to use the pen, as so much of what I do now is on a computer that the art of penmanship was way back in my past. I re-read what I had written and thought it was OK, but maybe not good enough. I wrote another card, with an apology, and the hope that the future will be better. I put it in the envelope and trotted off like an obedient student.

As I walked into the restaurant, I could smell the delicious freshly baked bread and croissants and the coffee brewing. I couldn't see Rachel, and was worried I had missed the 10.00am deadline. Then I saw her sitting in the corner wearing a hat.

It was a weird conversation. She was still pretending to be somebody else. I gave her the card I had written, which she seemed to be pleased with. Progress! I agreed we would get some professional help when we got back, and that seemed to be enough to end the arguments and conflict between us.

The next few days were good and relaxing. Rachel went off sailing and did her stuff, and left me to swim, play volleyball and chill. We met up for lunch and dinner, and had two lovely evenings drinking and watching the stars. It felt like the pressure was off, but getting back home was looming and I would have to open myself up to dealing with all of the past.

Chapter 25: Back to Reality - Rachel

Our last day in Grenada dawned, as all the others had, with the sun shining, the sounds of birds in the trees, and a beautiful smell of the herbs and flowers outside our room. In the distance I could hear the waves on the beach and the sounds of people just happy talking.

But I was lying in bed next to John, and realised this was a significant day. This was the day that marked a transition. A day which could be a beginning of a new and much better life – or the beginning of a very different life.

John was murmuring gently in his sleep, not close to waking up. I felt a need to get up, get moving and to make the best of our last day here, but I reached out and stroked his leg. He muttered and turned away from me. I felt disappointed, so I slid out of bed and went and stood on the balcony, taking in the sights and the sounds and the smells and the feelings around me. I knew what I did next could have a significant impact on our futures.

I pondered what had happened in the last two weeks. We seemed to have gone from a place where emotions were in a very narrow band, ranging between mediocrity and resentment to one where things seemed much more fragile. We had some surprising moments of closeness and love-making in the last few days; but those seemed to quickly swing from joy to anger. It felt like we had taken the lid off the bottle and the genie was out – and out of control.

I took a very deep breath and headed back into the room and went and sat on the edge of the bed on John's side. I reached across and stroked his hair. I wasn't sure what response I would get, but I was hoping for some connection with him, something that would tell me that at a subconscious level he was there for me and wanted me to be there for him. Still there was no response.

Feeling a little sad, I went and had a shower, and then started packing. When John heard me he started to stir. He then sat up in bed and looked at me a bit blankly. 'Rachel, what are you doing, it's early?'

'I have been trying to gently wake you, but you were fast asleep. Let's make the best of this day, because it may be a long time before we get to come somewhere like this again.'

'OK...if that's what you want. Let's go and have some breakfast.'

He got up, dressed in shorts and a rather grubby-looking t-shirt, and put on his flip flops.

I reached out and touched him on the elbow as we walked down to breakfast, but again got very little response. We sat down and breathed in the smell of freshly cooked bacon, croissants and bread, and looked at the piles of fruit. John loaded his plate up with croissants. I went and got some fresh fruit and yoghurt and granola, and some herbal tea, and there it was, on the table, a big contrast. John with his croissants and coffee, all beige and brown, and me with my healthier food of many different colours. Was this a sign of how different we were, of how different our lives were, and how different our desires were? Was I flogging a dead horse? The next few days would tell... I had no idea whether John was committed to changing anything and whether we could stay together, or whether we would be much better apart.

I watched John eating, crumbs going everywhere, slurping his coffee, eating with his mouth slightly open and felt estranged from him. Who was he? Did I really know him?

What I needed from him was a real commitment to making a change, and to making our relationship work; but all I had seen so far was brief attempts, thrown away quickly, and then him just getting back into his old patterns. I also looked down at my plate and thought, *What does this tell him about me, and who I am and what I really want?*

I went up to get some delicious, freshly squeezed orange juice, poured a glass for myself and poured a glass for John and took them back to the table. John looked at me and said, 'Oh, I was going to get some grapefruit juice.' My retort hovered in my mouth, but I smiled instead, went back and poured some grapefruit juice and carried it back to him. He grunted. Not even a thank you.

John finished eating his croissants, and returned for some more. He particularly liked the pain au raisin, and he got a couple of croissants with honey and one with Nutella – an endless gorging on carbohydrates. Just when I thought he couldn't eat any more, he went up to the hot plates and he asked for an omelette to be cooked for him – a cheese omelette with mushrooms and ham and peppers – and when it was cooked he brought it back with sausages and bacon on the side and, just in case the food was going to stop and he needed to stock up for the rest of his life, he went and got some waffles with maple syrup. By now our table for two was piled with his empty plates and littered with his crumbs, and there was I still sipping my orange juice.

To break the silence I finally said, 'OK, we've got until four o'clock before we need to get the car to the airport, and the flight leaves at six thirty. I'll go back and finish the packing so we're ready to go. What would you like to do for the rest of the day?'

John looked at me and said, 'I'm happy to relax in the sun, read my book, and have a nice lunch and a few cocktails. What would you like to do?'

'I would like to make the most of our time. I'd like to have a walk on the beach and go for a quick sail, too, and maybe do some snorkelling. John, would you like to do any of that with me?'

'Well, if you want to go sailing, that's fine, you do that. Maybe a walk on the beach after lunch, but not at the moment. I really want to go and lie down and relax.'

'See you at lunch, then,' I said, and walked slowly back to our room. I put all of John's dirty stuff into a plastic bag, put that into the suitcase and laid it on the bed ready for John to put whatever he wanted into it and to take out whatever clothes he needed for flying back.

I then headed down to the beach, wearing a sun hat because the sun was getting really hot. I enjoyed the feeling of the grains of sand between my toes, the warmth of the sand on the soles of my feet, and the sun on my shoulders and arms, filling me with warmth. *Wouldn't it be wonderful to have a husband or partner here, holding hands as we walked, I thought.*

But enough of the complaining; enough of the asking. Maybe I needed to give John the space to make his decision, and to make an effort to meet me in the life I wanted for us. If he wasn't prepared to do that, then that was his choice. All I could do was lay out the possibilities.

I sat down on the sand and felt so in tune with nature. There was nobody else around, just the blue sea, the blue sky, and the occasional white cloud drifting above. I felt the energy of the sun filling me. I lay down on the sand and thought deeply – not about the past, because I had done too much of that, but about the future, and the new Rachel...the Rachel who was herself. She was a mother, possibly a wife, but this Rachel had self-confidence, was doing things that gave her fulfilment and wasn't just a housewife. She wasn't somebody who went to the gym partly out of boredom and partly with the faint hope that one of the sleek, personal trainers, or even the tennis coach, would fancy her and give her some escape from the mundane life she was trapped in.

I was determined that when I got home I would start to be the new Rachel. I wouldn't fall back into the rut of my life. I would strive to achieve what was really important for me. If John wanted to join me, then that could be good; but I wasn't going to force him, as it just wouldn't work.

I got up and walked to where the boats were lent out and spoke to the guy in charge of the sailing boats and the canoes, and said I fancied a sail. He rigged up one of the catamarans, and I put on a life jacket and climbed on board. He pushed me out, and with a big smile and a wave I headed off through the gentle waves out into the bay. I felt very much at one with the waves and the wind. I clipped on the trapeze, sheeted the sails, and climbed out onto the side and hurtled off into the distance, feeling the spray of the waves on my body and the wind in my hair. I whooped with joy, and the sense of freedom, and being in control. *If I keep heading west*, I thought, *I could make it to Panama, but that could take a week or more and I don't have any water or any food. Maybe I need to head back sometime, but there's no hurry.* I carried on until the hotel and the beach were like a postcard in the distance. I then went back on to the trampoline and clipped myself in, tacked around and headed back. I had a real sense of my life taking a totally new direction, with me in control, with fun and fulfilment. It felt powerful; it felt wonderful; it felt really compelling.

I hurtled back in on the waves, looked up at just the right moment and pulled the rudders up. One of the boat boys came running out to grab the bows. He helped me down off the hull, and smiled and said, 'Wow, that was good, well done!' Glowing with pride, I walked up the beach, put the life jacket back and thanked him. 'I've had a great time. Thank you for looking after me!'

I headed back to the pool and saw John lying on the sunbed, reading the same book, the same legal thriller he'd been reading on the flight out and the whole time we'd been here. *Gosh, he must read really slowly, and why on earth, when he is a lawyer, does he want to read a thriller about lawyers?* I thought. *What does that say about his view of the world and his limited horizons?*

But the new Rachel decided, Why should I get upset about that? Why should I criticise John for what he reads? Why don't I just focus on what is important for me, and what's going to make me feel happy and fulfilled?

I went up to John, leant over him and kissed him on the forehead. The lips would have felt a little bit too intimate; a kiss on the forehead was showing a desire for connection but not giving too much away – not giving too much away to be rejected by him.

He put his book down. 'Fancy a drink?' he smiled.

'OK. Let's go to the pool bar.'

We swam across and looked at the list of cocktails for the day. Today's special was a strawberry daiquiri, which felt vaguely healthy, so I asked for two of those. I noticed for the first time that the straws were paper, which was good, although if you drank too slowly they started to go soggy – maybe an incentive to finish the drink quickly and order another. We sat there side by side in semi-companionable silence, with our arms touching.

'It's a shame this is all coming to an end,' I said. 'It has been a lovely place to be, and I know we've had some difficult conversations, but also think we've had some really important experiences.'

'Yeah.'

OK, I thought, *ever the man of few words. I wonder what he's really thinking? Maybe I should ask him.*

I know I'd said I wasn't going to push him, but I needed to know. 'What are you feeling, John?' I ventured.

'Oh, not much.'

Shall I let him get away with that? Maybe I should let him know how I'm feeling?

I touched him on the arm and said, 'I'm feeling good, John. I'm really glad we came here. Many things are much clearer to me, and it's also allowed me time to work out what I really want, and the Rachel I want to be in the future – and she's going to be very different from the Rachel who has been around up till now. Talking to Olivia and Richard opened my eyes to how we've been, and also made me start to think about what the possibilities are in the future. I know what I want, but what I'm not sure about is what you really want, and how much you are prepared to commit to making our relationship work. I really think we need to work together to answer that.'

I saw John gulp, and he looked down and he said, 'Oh, so what do you want me to do?'

'It's about what you want to do, John. I know what I want, and

I would love us to be in a great, loving relationship. Remaining how we are now won't work for me. So this is a chance for you to take charge of your destiny, for you to make a commitment to what it is you want – and if that is with me, that would be wonderful; but if you just want to drift, then you are going to drift alone, I'm afraid.'

John took a long drink, draining his glass, and made his usual annoying slurping noise, but I let that pass. 'Yeah, I know,' he said. 'It's been really painful for me to come to the realisation how much has been wrong in the last few years, of us not being connected and drifting apart, but I do love you and I would like to be with you. I would like to try and be the person I think you want me to be, but I need to think about it more. I am not as impulsive as you. I am much more logical and methodical, and I need to go through that process, because the worst thing would be for me to pretend I can be everything you want and not be true to myself. I need to find myself, and what I want, because in the last forty or so years I have been doing things I thought other people wanted me to do. I have wasted my life trying to be the son I thought my parents wanted. So I've got one hell of a way to go.'

I was stunned. This was the most John had said in the whole two weeks we had been here; in fact, in months, and probably years. I stayed quiet, wondering what he would say next.

'Please give me a bit of time, Rachel. Let me do this the way I need to do it.'

Part of me was thinking, What the hell do you need to come to a decision? What 'way' do you need to do this? But part of me was also thinking, as I had before, There's no point in forcing this; it's got to come from him, and I just need to take a step back and allow him to do whatever he needs to do.

'OK,' I said, 'just relax and enjoy the rest of the day, and we'll see what the next few days bring. Fancy some lunch?'

With what John had had for breakfast a few hours ago, I imagined he couldn't possibly eat anything for lunch, but this was a day when the buffet was on, and wow, what a choice! And it was all so beautifully arranged it almost seemed a shame to spoil what had been created. I tucked in and had some delicious smoked salmon and bread and lots of salad. John came to the table with a plate groaning under the weight of steak and potatoes and bread. I looked at his bulging stomach, again; but had to remind myself that it was his choice, again. My choice was to look after myself. I love my food, but I love the food that loves me.

We sat chatting about this and that; about what we thought James, Jenny and Rowena had been up to while we were away; about what our parents might have changed in the house, and about John going back to work.

No questions were really asked about me, or what I wanted, or what I was going to do, or who this new Rachel was. I was wondering whether John was just blissfully unaware of how determined I was to change, or just couldn't cope with the idea of me being different.

The afternoon passed quietly, with John on his sunbed with John Grisham. I finished the packing, but also took time to stroll around, enjoying the beauty one last time. I then went to John and suggested he go back to the room and have a shower and get changed ready for our departure. But he insisted on reading a few more pages of his book. I sat there patiently, wondering precisely how long it took to read 'a few more pages', but didn't say anything.

Finally, he got up and walked back with me to the room; but he didn't get changed, he sat there in his slightly damp shorts and grubby t-shirt. I suggested to him he might get a bit cold, and even uncomfortable, sitting on an aircraft for hours in wet, salt-stained shorts, and with much reluctance he changed into something more suitable.

I closed our suitcases and asked John to carry them down to the entrance. He did, albeit grumpily, and the wheels went clack-clack-clack on the cobbles. There was a small group of people at the entrance, waiting for the bus to come and take us the short distance to the airport. I got talking to a couple, and we exchanged thoughts about what our holiday had been like. They said they'd had a wonderful time, and I could see from the way they were hanging onto each other how close they were. John seemed to be miles away from me, although he was in touching distance.

The bus turned up, and the driver handed us all cool bottles of water, loaded up our suitcases, and we were on our way. At the airport we were met by lots of locals offering to wheel our suitcases the twenty feet from the bus to the entrance – for a price – and I politely declined. When we checked in, I was hoping we might get upgraded, as it would have been great to fly first class and have some leg room, and be able to lie back and sleep, but John didn't even try asking, despite me giving him meaningful looks.

We boarded and flew the short distance to St Lucia to pick up other passengers, and then settled for the long haul. We barely spoke, as John immediately put his headphones on and started watching a movie. I read, and tried to sleep, and we both ate tasteless airline food, without comment. And then the lady in front of me dropped her seat into full recline, and put her headphones on too – and all I could hear was the irritating, tinny sound of her music for hours, her head practically in my lap. John seemed oblivious, and fell asleep, with another movie running. I had to climb over him to go to the toilet a couple of times, but he didn't even notice – or else was just ignoring me. I felt my energy draining from me, and dreaded landing.

We landed at Gatwick. It was grey; it looked cold; it was drizzling. I started to think about what it was going to be like back at home, and whether it would feel like home, and what the next few days would bring. John was sitting upright. The plane taxied and then stopped, and everyone stood up, including John, scrabbling for possessions, waiting for the doors to open, which seemed to take ages. I just sat and waited. There was more waiting at the baggage claim, and whilst we slowly moved through Passport Control. Our arranged car wasn't there when we arrived at the taxi rank, and John asked me why. I wanted to know why it was I always had to organise everything, and sort it out when it went wrong. I called the company: they were five minutes away.

We rang the doorbell, because John had forgotten our house keys, and my parents appeared.

My mother looked at me, a bit surprised. 'Oh, we weren't expecting you until later?' she said.

I tried to smile. 'Well, we're back.'

'Did you have a nice time?'

'Yes, lovely,' I said, as we manoeuvred ourselves and our luggage through the door, knowing that giving her any more details would create problems. Best to pretend it had all been wonderful.

'Good,' she said. 'Lunch will be ready at 12.30.'

'How are the children?'

'James is out with his friends, I think. Jennifer we haven't seen. She might still be in bed. And Rowena has been getting very excited about seeing you. She's in the garden drawing pictures.'

With that the back door burst open and Woody came in, wagging his tail furiously. I knelt down and gave him a big hug. And then Rowena came rushing through the door and leapt at me and cried, 'Mummy, Mummy, Mummy! I missed you!'

John hadn't really spoken, and was just standing beside me, looking a bit left out.

We carried the bags upstairs and I got out the things we'd bought for the children – the stuff most people buy for their children when they've been away: a t-shirt for James, some coral jewellery for Jennifer, and a t-shirt and hat for Rowena.

When we went back downstairs my mother was fussing around, and my father was sitting reading the newspaper, like he seemed to spend most of his life doing. That and waiting for the six o'clock news to start. We sat down and had lunch – a rather different lunch to the ones we'd been enjoying for the last two weeks, but my mum had made an effort. She seemed to have forgotten all the things I don't like, but hey-ho.

After lunch I went upstairs and knocked on Jennifer's door. No answer. I opened the door and there she was in bed, curtains drawn, playing on her iPhone. Annoyance swept over me and I went up to her and said, 'Hi, Jenny, how are you, have you had a good time without your mum at home?'

She mumbled, hardly looking at me, 'Yeah, suppose so.'

This is the lot of a mother of teenage children, I thought, *I'm not alone.* 'Do you know where James has gone?' I asked.

'Yeah, he said he was going out with some of his creepy friends. He will be back at dinnertime.'

'OK, Jenny, get dressed, and let's go downstairs. I have presents for you.'

'Oh, OK.'

I went back downstairs and she followed shortly afterwards, still half-asleep and half-dressed. We all sat down, trying to play happy families: my father, who'd had an affair; my mother, who'd decided that she just needed 'to suck it up and live with it'; my eleven-year-old daughter, who I didn't really know, and seemed to belong to a different world, a different planet; and Rowena, who was wonderfully effusive and bouncy, and who seemed to love life. And then there was John, my husband, at the moment, and of course Woody, who loved everyone without question.

So that was it. The homecoming. Not quite what I had hoped for, but it was OK.

We spent the afternoon catching up with emails, and sorting out the post – although this consisted only of bills and junk mail. It made me think of the postmen who delivered this stuff. It used to be a noble occupation, bringing news of love and happiness, births and invites to weddings. It felt sad that their role had been reduced to carrying around bags full of junk mail and brown envelopes. All important stuff appeared electronically, in the blink of an eye on a screen, to either be 'liked' or ignored.

The evening came. James turned up looking like James has done for some while – a bit disinterested, a bit disengaged. But I got a half-hearted hug. He took one look at the t-shirt we had brought for him and said thank you and put it down. I tried to talk to him about what he'd been up to, but he just said, 'Not much'. I asked him about the coming week, and he said, 'Don't know.' I wondered where that level of enthusiasm would take him in life...

My parents asked all the right questions – where we had been, what we had seen, who we had spoken to – and I guess I played it a bit like James, not wanting to give them any details, not wanting to talk about the deep and significant stuff, because that wasn't the planet they were on. They just wanted platitudes.

By about eight o'clock I was feeling tired, and John had work the next day so we went to bed about nine o'clock. We undressed in silence and got into bed, next to each other, but miles apart. I fell asleep before I had the chance to say anything to John.

I work up early. John was beginning to stir, and then the alarm went off at six o'clock and it was time for him to get up, get into a suit, and head into London. He went through the process he has done for so many days and so many weeks and so many years, since I have known him. But this time I went downstairs and made some coffee and toast for him; and just before he went out of the door I touched him on the shoulder and said, 'Have a lovely day, and remember what comes next.'

He looked puzzled at first, and then said, 'Yeah, OK. I'll see you later.'

Chapter 26: Back to Reality - John

I awoke with a sense of dread. Rachel was looking down at me, and for a moment I didn't know where I was. Then I realised: it was the last day of our holiday. Rachel was in a strange place; she was pressing me to make big changes. But I really didn't know who this person was any more, and I really didn't know what I wanted. She was trying to be affectionate, but part of me was trying to avoid being rejected again.

Comfort eating felt a good place to be. The croissants and coffee, they were really great. I could see Rachel looking at me as if she wanted to say something, but I thought, *To hell with it, I am enjoying this. I'm going to keep on eating. Eating keeps me away from the uncertainty. I'm best friends with croissants and coffee.*

Then Rachel brought me some orange juice. Doesn't she know I don't like orange juice? Why on earth didn't she bring me grapefruit juice? Then, having eaten lots of carbohydrates, I thought maybe some protein was needed – an omelette and all the trimmings beckoned. I loved the way they cooked them right there in front of you, with whatever you wanted in them. The omelette man, that was his job, and he did it with a big smile on his face. What a great, simple job to have. Just being in this beautiful place, responding to people's requests for cheese, more cheese, less cheese, tomatoes, herbs, mushrooms, peppers, potatoes, maybe even smoked salmon... No commuting for hours every day, no dealing with clients whose needs were uncertain, and who bristled at the cost and rarely said thank you. Maybe I could apply for a job out here; maybe I could tell Rachel I had found the life I wanted, and I'd see her next year when she came out with the kids. Or maybe not.

Rachel wanted to go and be busy. She wanted to go walking. She wanted to go sailing. I wanted to relax and enjoy the last day here before I had to go back to work on Monday, sitting on the same train, in the same carriage, in the same seat, next to the same people who never speak to you. God, the twitching newspapers, the irritating people with their headphones in listening to music...rap music...crap music. The same people who look at you and through you; the same people who avoid your glance, and who, if you died in front of them, would probably just walk away. What a strange world we inhabit.

Rachel and I went our separate ways. I went to lie down to read my book. How slowly I seemed to read compared to how quickly I could scan legal documents; but then it took me to a different place, with different sorts of people. It was good to escape from my everyday life and enjoy the sunshine – and the courtrooms of America.

After a few hours of busyness Rachel reappeared, gave me a kiss on the forehead, which I supposed was good news. An invitation back to the bedroom would have been even nicer, but that was never going to come. And off we went to lunch. Wow, the staff had really pushed the boat out this time. The tables were groaning with seafood – prawns, crab, lobsters – and salads and stuff. There were steaks and chops and chicken cooking on a barbeque. I could have stayed there all day, but I guessed that wouldn't have gone down too well. The great thing about all-you-can-eat buffets is you can eat it all, and you can eat until you don't realise you are actually full – about half an hour ago. I tried to forget I would have to spend quite a few hours on the plane next to Rachel, but still we enjoyed lunch. We chatted and seemed to be quite relaxed.

I knew Rachel was waiting for me to say something significant; was wanting me to voice my commitment to us being different. And then she started talking, and my heart sank. I thought this was going to be a 'Goodbye, John. It's been great, but I'm off' type of speech. Maybe it was the PT instructor or the tennis coach? But no, she left me hanging. She told me she loved me, which was really good to hear. She told me she wanted a future with me, but it was really down to me. She said she knew what she wanted in the future. *If you know what you want, why don't you tell me? Why do I have to guess? I thought.*

I tried to respond to her as well as I could, saying stuff like, 'Yeah, I understand, it's not been great' and 'I do know things need to be different'. One of the things I love about Rachel is her energy and enthusiasm, and the way she can make decisions and jump straight in to a thing. I tried to explain to her that that wasn't me; I need to think about things. Hell, I'm a lawyer! I don't just need to think about things, I need to see things in writing; I need to see evidence from the past of whether this is the right way to go or the wrong way to go; I need to listen to experts' opinions. And this counselling thing certainly wasn't something I could decide about in a moment. She seemed to get that, which was good, but it made me feel the next few days would be the decider upon which our whole future lay, and I needed to work out what I really wanted.

With that weight on my shoulders, I realised we only had a couple of hours before we needed to be packed and gone, so I went back to the room. Rachel had finished the packing and told me I needed to take off my t-shirt and swimming shorts and put something slightly more appropriate on. I was about to pick up the cases when Rachel suggested to me that I pick up the cases. I thought that was pretty obvious. Isn't that what men normally do? So I carried the cases down. What happened to the days of suitcases without wheels, anyway? The days of real men – or even servants – who carried them rather than wheeling them along making that annoying clacking noise? Anyway, ours had wheels. And have wheels, will transport.

There were people trying to con us out of money to carry our bags the few feet to the airport entrance when we arrived, but I brushed them off and went and stood in the check-in queue.

One thing that always really irritated me about Rachel is

that when we got to check-in queues, she always stood in front, trying to take control. Where did that put me, the man? This time, surprisingly, she stood back and allowed me to go first, and the lady did her stuff on the computer. *What is it they do on that computer?* I wondered, as she sat there tapping away. Anyway, when she handed me our boarding passes I looked at them and thought, *Oh, that's a shame, we're not up top.*

We went through security and into the departure lounge, which was pretty full. Rachel read a book – one of the many books she had brought with her. I wandered around the shops and looked at the sort of stuff you can buy in an airport duty free shop in Grenada. Rachel had already bought stuff for the kids, though, and I couldn't see any Toblerone.

Rachel was a bit edgy on the flight, and annoyed that the person in front of her had dropped their seat right back, but I thought, *Hey, we've got eleven hours to go, I'll watch a few films, maybe have a sleep.* I could hear Rachel huffing and puffing, but I carried on watching my movie. She climbed over me several times to go to the toilet, not very carefully it seemed, which woke me up, which was annoying.

Our luggage was ages arriving, and the car Rachel had booked wasn't there on time, so we had to wait in the drizzle. I hadn't taken our house keys, so we rang the doorbell of our own house and David and Kathleen came to the front door – and it felt as if it was their house, not ours.

The conversation was a bit stilted over lunch. David and I have never really got on that well; he is a man of few words who likes reading The Daily Telegraph and muttering about stuff. He doesn't really like rugby, either, so we have little to talk about. Rowena came bouncing in; so did Woody, Rachel's dog, shedding hairs everywhere. Jenny was upstairs sleeping, and James was out somewhere, so we didn't see them till later.

About nine o'clock we both agreed we would go up to bed. I was not looking forward to being back in a suit, back on my tiresome commute to hours of work, and then the long commute home. But the weight of Rachel's expectations on me... Something needed to shift, I knew, but it looked like it was down to me, as always.

Rachel got up for once and made me some coffee. I think she wanted to talk to me, but I was in the commuting zone, briefcase full of stuff, ready to go. She said something about remembering what was next... I didn't really know what she meant, so said I'd see her later. Maybe I do know, though.

The receptionist seemed pleased to see me, and so did my secretary, and I started going through my emails, all fifty-six of them. Two hours later I realised how insignificant most of them were. How much of my time is taken up with insignificance? I wondered.

I started considering the life I wanted, which needed to be different from this. Work, for so many years, had been on the treadmill, wanting to become an equity partner in a law firm so that friends, colleagues and people at the rugby club could look up to me and say, 'Wow, hasn't John achieved great things.' Now that seemed rather empty, rather pointless.

Nineteen or so years ago I had started this journey, with Rachel, in love, full of hope, full of dreams, thinking that once I had got to where I was now life would be wonderful; but all I was doing was running even faster on the treadmill to keep going, to keep the expensive house going, keep the expensive children going, to buy more stuff to try to make Rachel happy, to make me happy, and that wasn't working.

Tears started to form in my eyes and then roll down my cheeks, and I buried my head in my hands and sobbed. Trying to hide my face with some papers, I headed for the men's room and splashed my face with cold water. Back at my desk I got out some paper and a pen and started writing lists of what I wanted, and lists of what I didn't want. I filled pages, and what was strange, was that the stuff I wanted was more about feelings than about stuff. I wanted to be loved. I wanted to love. I wanted closeness, and I wanted a feeling of being worthwhile, of doing something worthwhile. That was weird, because it was the first time in my life I had ever sat down and started thinking about these things.

I then went for a walk to a nearby park and sat on a bench. It was cold and grey, but dry, and I thought about what a difference in view there was between today and two days' ago. What a difference in the weather; what a difference in the outlook; what a difference in the world I was in. Breathing deeply, the smell of diesel and petrol fumes hit me. Was this where I wanted to spend the next twenty or so years? I took my phone out of my pocket and sent a text to Rachel. It just said, *I love you.* I pressed Send. I waited for a reply. Waited five minutes, ten minutes. No reply. I walked back to work, got in the lift, went upstairs, went into my office, and sat in front of my computer. But I just couldn't concentrate.

I looked at my phone again. Still no reply from Rachel. I re-read my lists of things I wanted and didn't want. *I wanted to be loved. I want to love.* And I remembered all the stuff we had been told by Richard and Olivia. Maybe that was where we needed to start. I knew that was what Rachel had been pushing me to do.

I started searching on the internet for marriage counselling, and pages and pages of people came up, but nothing sounded remotely like what Richard and Olivia had told us. I then remembered I had Richard's number, and that he'd quietly said, 'Call me anytime.'

He seemed pleased to hear from me, and after our general hellos, I told him we'd had an 'interesting' time in Grenada, and that we'd really enjoyed talking to them. I then took a deep breath, and asked him if he still had the number of the couple they had seen ten years ago. He promised me he would text it to me, and their website address. As we said goodbye, there was mention of dinner, which I agreed would be great, and then Richard said again, 'Call me anytime.' I ended the call, and took another deep breath.

A couple of minutes later a text came through and, before I had time to change my mind, I dialled the number.

'Hello, it's Neil here, how can I help?' said a soft, calm voice.

He listened, and he helped me to explain how I was feeling, what had been happening and what I wanted. I talked for twenty minutes and, for the first time in my life, I felt somebody was really listening to me, somebody who really wanted to help and wasn't judging me.

He then explained how they work, what they would do, and it sounded intriguing – and it sounded like they could help. He asked if I had any questions and I obviously wanted to know the cost. He told me, and I was surprised, but then I thought about how much I charge to help people with their legal stuff, and how much these people were charging for changing people's lives, and there was no comparison. He offered to speak to Rachel, if she wanted to talk, and I asked him when they could see us. He suggested one evening next week, and I said I would speak to Rachel and call back as soon as I could.

I felt lighter. I felt there was hope. And I felt there was somebody out there who could help us work out what we both wanted and how to work together to achieve that. Everything else in the office – the emails, the piles of papers, all the other stuff – all that seemed insignificant compared to love, life and the future.

I went home that evening feeling different and, for the first time I could recall in many, many months, I walked in through the front door with a smile on my face. Rachel was there – her parents, thank God, had gone – and James, Jenny and Rowena were all sitting round the table waiting for dinner. Something was cooking on the hob, and Rachel came up to me, gave me a hug and a kiss on the cheek, and said, 'Welcome back. How was your day?' We had dinner together and it was good – not as good as the food on holiday, but it was OK. We talked about the holiday, and the fun stuff we had done, and the kids seemed genuinely interested; and then they told us what they'd been doing while we were away, and stuff that their grandpa and grandma had done which made them laugh, or made them annoyed. They had been OK with them, they had been safe, and they had even had some fun, which was good to hear.

They then went up to their rooms to connect with their electronic netherworld – well, James and Jenny did; Rowena was probably drawing or colouring – and Rachel got a bottle of wine, poured two glasses, and asked, 'How did you get on today?'

I told her I had spoken to Neil and liked what he'd said, and that I thought it would be a good place for us to try and work through some stuff, perhaps as soon as next week.

Rachel looked really pleased, and thanked me. 'That probably wasn't easy for you,' she said, 'but I really do appreciate it, and thank you for your message as well. It made me feel much better, but I wanted to respond in person.' And then she came and wrapped her arms around me and gave me a big hug. And life, in that moment, felt so much more hopeful.

Chapter 27: The First Session - John

I made the appointment for Thursday evening next week at five o'clock. Neil told me the session would be about three-and-a-half hours long and we'd be talking about what had happened to get us to where we are now. Not just the last thirteen years of our marriage, but also our previous relationships, and how we felt it had brought us to our current situation. It felt scary, the thought of going off to a meeting with people I didn't know to talk about our lives – and probably talk about intimate things, as well, that I've never spoken to anyone about. I kept having to take deep breaths.

When I told Rachel I had made the booking she was really pleased. She came and gave me a big hug and a kiss and said, 'Thank you, it must be difficult for you, but this is really important,' so that made me feel good. They sent us details beforehand, including a form to fill in with all sorts of information and some slightly odd questions. It included a bit of personal history and whether we had any medical problems, and asked us to rate things from one to ten in terms of our relationship. We had to state what the problem was, how it had come about, what we wanted, and how we would know when we had it. It took me ages to complete the form, as well as the timeline of our life from birth, including significant events. We were instructed not to share it with each other, but I was intrigued to know what Rachel would have on hers.

The place was about an hour away, and I drove. Rachel sat next to me not really saying anything. I was nervous, not sure what to expect, or where this would lead us to. I put some music on – some opera. But Rachel hates opera, so I quickly turned it off again.

Rachel turned to me and said, 'Do you want to talk or listen to some music?'

'I am happy to talk. What would you like to talk about?'

Rachel then started talking about what she wanted, what had happened to us in the last couple of weeks, and just how much she would like things to work out for us, if we could make it work. That gave me a bit of hope, but I also hung onto the 'if we could make it work' bit and started to think that maybe this was a gentle way of Rachel ending it. I was not sure how I would cope with that. All we could do was see where this took us.

In the silence that followed, I turned the radio on a couple of times, but the music didn't feel right. I could feel Rachel clearly wasn't enjoying it. We pulled into the town of Lymington and found the offices. They weren't quite what I expected, but Neil and Maria were waiting for us at the top of a large staircase. They both smiled and said hello and shook our hands, and then took us into a large room with lots of books, comfortable chairs and a settee – it was very different to my workplace, or the various offices where I saw clients. It felt relaxed but professional, and, actually, in a strange way, it felt sort of good. They invited us to sit wherever we liked, and we chose the settee – although sat a distance away from each other.

Neil and Maria weren't quite what I expected either, but exuded a deep sense of calm, and, weirdly, I felt safe. Yes, I felt this was a place where I could be open and tell it all. The way they both spoke seemed to flow from one to the other quite naturally. Nobody was in charge, and it was almost like a duet, with both playing alongside each other and then one playing their solo, followed by a pause, and the other one playing their solo. It was like listening to two masters at work, which again was very different to the way I was used to working.

They thanked us for the information we had sent, and explained how they would work with us. This session was to understand how we had got to where we were right now, and what unhelpful patterns had been set up in our relationship and in previous ones. They emphasised the confidentiality and lack of judgement, and that the more open and honest we could be, the more they could help us.

Fundamentally, we had three choices: to continue as we were; to separate; or to really invest time and effort into creating a new and different relationship that acknowledged we were different people than the couple that met eighteen years ago, now that life, work and children had all had an impact. This was not about putting a sticking plaster on the old; this was about fundamental change for something new.

They asked us to take it in turns talking through the past, from the moment we met, and what had happened from then on. What had been significant? What had been the major positives and the major negatives? We were asked not to interrupt each other, because in relationships there are always at least two perspectives, and they are both equally right, and often very different. What was important was really hearing the other, as this would begin to build the trust we would need to share our thoughts in a safe space. We agreed we would do that, and were asked who would like to go first.

Rachel said she would like me to go first, and I said I would like Rachel to go first, and there was an awkward pause and we both sort of laughed, and I said, 'OK, I will go first.'

I started talking, and wasn't sure how much detail was needed, but was sure I would get asked questions if there wasn't enough. So, I began, detailing my life with Rachel in a few minutes...

'I first met Rachel when I was in my last year. I was twenty-one and was at a rugby club party at Warwick University and, like pretty much all rugby club parties, there was a lot of booze, a lot of boy stuff and a lot of riotous partying. I'd had lots of girlfriends, but I was single at that time and saw Rachel on the other side of the room, and there was just something about her that attracted me. She looked pretty hot, and seemed to be on her own, so I went over to her. I was reasonably sober at that point, and introduced myself, and we got talking about university and the courses we were doing. Rachel was doing something called Management Sciences, which sounded a bit dull – mind you, law was pretty dull. I got her a drink, we carried on talking, and then we had a quick dance and started to get intimate, so we kissed and I offered to walk her home. We were both on campus, and somehow we ended up at my place. I made her some coffee, and she seemed up for it, so we made love, and it felt good, really good.

'We did lots of things together after that, and we had good fun. Our friends got on with each other and we liked doing similar activities. She was quite sporty, but didn't play rugby. I carried on with my rugby but, as she was a year behind me, I graduated and moved down to London. I had a training contract with a firm of solicitors, and we kept in touch, phoned each other a couple of times a week, and she came down to see me. Every few weekends I went up to see her and it seemed to be a good rhythm, it worked well. I was getting busy with work and Rachel was focusing on her finals – she had a job lined up with Unilever – and when she graduated it seemed the right thing to move in together.

'We were both in London so we found a nice flat in Putney, on the second floor of an old converted Victorian building with a noisy fire escape entrance to it. It was pretty old and tired, but had lovely, solid, big rooms – which were cold as there was no central heating, just electric fires – with crappy old furniture, but that didn't seem to matter. We got into the swing of work and the fun stuff, too; but the partying sort of faded until it was just weekends, and then became sometimes at weekends, but we were focused on our careers and it was good to be with her.

'Life carried on for about four years doing that stuff. I was slowly progressing up the ladder, and Rachel was doing well. And then Rachel got pregnant and that was a real Oh shit! moment for me, because I thought Rachel was on the pill so I hadn't taken any precautions, and our sex life had been good, pretty frequent.

'When Rachel told me she was pregnant she had a smile on her face, but I could see she was a bit worried at how I would take it. She asked me what I thought we should do. That was a really difficult moment for me, because having a child was in my plans somewhere, but this seemed a bit soon: how would it affect Rachel and how would it affect me? I asked her what she would like to do, and she said she would like to have the baby. I was sure we could cope with that, but thought we had better get married, because my parents wouldn't like it if we weren't married and had a baby.

'We quickly arranged to get married in the register office in two weeks' time. A few friends came along to witness it, and we went down to the pub afterwards for a quick bite and some drinks. That weekend we went off to Paris for a couple of nights, which was nice, but it wasn't the ideal honeymoon. But I was busy at work, and Rachel was busy at work, and we couldn't change our plans to take a couple of weeks off. I couldn't really afford it, either.

'James was born the following March, and I had an important client meeting that day and asked Rachel, or the hospital, to give me a call when the baby was due to be born. We were expecting a fairly easy birth, and Rachel went into Charing Cross Hospital. Later I got the phone call asking me to come in to the hospital, as Rachel was about to give birth, so I got on the District line and the train stopped at Earls Court. The next train took bloody ages, so by the time I got to the hospital it was all over.

'Rachel wasn't earning now, so I had to work even harder to make the money to pay for the baby, as well as all the bills. The flat really wasn't suitable for a baby, as we couldn't get a pushchair up and down the stairs, and there wasn't really room for all the equipment, so we started looking for a house to buy. We found a three-bed house in Twickenham. The price wasn't bad because it was under the Heathrow flight path and it needed a lot done to it. I launched into DIY, which wasn't my best area, but I bodged things up and painted and tried plastering, which was interesting. I thought it looked easy, so I bought all the equipment, bought the plaster, mixed it up and spread it over the wall and thought it looked OK. I went to get a cup of coffee and came back five minutes later and couldn't understand why there was a big pile of wet plaster on the floor? It had just slid off the wall? So I had to get a plasterer in to finish that, and a plumber to do the bathroom, but I finished the painting, which was OK. I don't think it was Rachel's ideal, but it was good enough.

'James was growing up and getting noisier, and he needed a lot of Rachel's time and attention, so sex went off the agenda. I got home late and left early, and didn't see much of them. Even at the weekends I was busy working on cases. It was interesting watching James grow up, though, and I guess I was an OK dad in the time I had available.

'Just when things started to settle down a bit Rachel got pregnant again – and this was sort of planned, because we thought it would be nice for James to have a brother or sister. We hoped it might quieten him down a bit! Rachel had joined the local group of the NCT – the National Childbirth Trust – and went to the twice-weekly meetings and coffee mornings and drinks evenings, and she would come home bright-eyed from all they had been told about how to have natural births and how to bring up the baby in a healthy way. She said she wanted a home birth this time, and the midwife seemed OK with that, so we bought a birthing pool and whale music and candles and all that stuff.

'We got ready for a home birth. I filled up the pool, and Rachel got in, and then things started to get difficult, and the midwife said she was sorry but the baby was getting a little bit distressed and we needed to go to the hospital. The blue lights came, and off Rachel went with the midwife to Charing Cross. I followed in the car, and I sat outside the delivery room, on one of those awful hard chairs under the bright, fluorescent lights, wondering what was happening. Nobody came to tell me. And then the midwife came out and said – and it sounds really corny – "Congratulations, you've got a baby girl, do you want to come and see her?" I went in and there was this shrivelled thing clasped to Rachel's chest, and it was crying, and here was Jennifer.

'She was difficult, and cried all the time, so I didn't really take to her for a long time because I kept getting woken up in the night. And Rachel was tired and had James to look after, and when she heard the crying she would nudge me and ask me to deal with her, to go and give her a bottle of milk because she couldn't breastfeed her. Sometimes I would get up, but sometimes I was so tired from working long hours that I just couldn't, so things got pretty tense between us. There were quite a lot of arguments, and we didn't have much time together. There was not much fun, either, and I felt I was paying out money to buy stuff and keep the house going, with not much gratitude, and when I got home at night Rachel didn't often seem pleased to see me. I often had to bite my tongue.

'Rachel wasn't happy, and we had lots of arguments about stuff – why was I messy? why didn't I hang my clothes up? why didn't I do my fair share of looking after the children? why didn't I do the washing? why didn't I do the ironing? It was a tough time. My parents were really good. They would come and spend time with us, and they even offered to babysit so we could go out and enjoy ourselves. But we were both too tired, and Rachel wasn't very happy leaving them with my parents. Her parents weren't available very much, or much help, so that was all difficult.

'I felt we needed to get away, and I booked a long weekend in New York, as Rachel had always wanted to go there, and I had too. I booked three nights at a lovely hotel and arranged for my parents to look after Jennifer and James. Rachel was reluctant, but we went. When we got to our hotel room, after the seven-hour flight, Rachel looked out the window, entranced by the view, and kept saying thank you, thank you. It was the first time, for a long time, I had felt she was genuinely grateful, and that felt good.

'That weekend, the barriers sort of tumbled down, and I took her in my arms and we made love for the first time in I couldn't remember how long – and it was like having my old Rachel back. We walked round Central Park; we visited the Museum of Modern Art, which Rachel wanted to go and see, and the library, and had lots of experiences – even the cheesy tourist stuff, like going on the bus to tour around the Bronx and different parts of New York. It was great, and every night we made love. And even in the middle of the night we made love, and we made love again in the morning. I reckon in those three days we made love more often than we had in the last seven or eight years!

'We got home and got back into the swing of things – or the rut of things – and then one day, a couple of months later, Rachel told me she was pregnant and that she couldn't cope with another baby. She thought the best thing would be to have an abortion. But I thought that one more wouldn't be that different, and what would my parents think if Rachel had an abortion? They would hate it. I couldn't do that. We agreed she would have it and a few months later Rowena was born. It was a straightforward birth and she was very different. She was very calm, and I could see the mischief in her eyes. I was there when she was born and it was an incredible experience as I had never realised birth was quite like that. The midwife passed Rowena to me before she passed her to Rachel, and it was one of the most magical moments of my life, just holding this baby that I had helped create, in my arms, and I was the first parent to hold her! I passed her to Rachel, and it was good.

'Then we got home and it was difficult with James, with Jennifer. I think they both felt jealous of the new baby, because it was taking all the attention. Rachel was unhappy. I don't know why. She found it hard to get out of bed in the morning; she found it hard to look after the children. And there I was, off to work every day – and working really hard to make partner so I could buy us a bigger house to live in.

'I'd get back and the place was a mess, and Rachel looked a mess, and the children were not in bed and fighting with each other. I suggested to Rachel she should go and see the doctor, and she told me she had been, and the doctor had prescribed her some anti-depressants but she'd thrown them in the bin. We had an argument about that and I said, "What is the point of going to see the doctor if you are not going to take their advice?"

'Rachel got talking to her friends at NCT, and they invited her to join the local gym, which was bloody expensive, which meant I had another set of fees to pay. She went along but I don't know what she did. She said she wanted to go and lose some weight, but she stayed pretty much the same.

'Life carried on like that, really. There was a lot of tension between us, the children were getting older, and I was spending the week working and the weekends at the rugby club, as I had to get some escape from all of this stuff. On Sundays we would do family stuff, like take the children out for a walk along the river, or have lunch at a pub or at home. We didn't really talk much and certainly didn't make love very much.

'A few years later I got promoted to partner, which was what I had been struggling all these years to make, which meant a lot more money – but even more bloody work. I was still commuting into London every day and, one evening, when I got back, Rachel told me she thought we needed to move to a bigger house. Our three-bedroomed house was a bit full, and we did need separate bedrooms for the kids, and it would be nice if they had a playroom downstairs so I could have somewhere tidy to rest when I got back from work.

'We started looking and found somewhere in East Horsley. The price seemed ridiculous, way out of our reach, but I had been talking to my parents about it and they said they wanted to help. They had no one else to give the money to, so they helped us buy the house. Once again, it needed a lot doing to it, and I was the one who had to organise it somehow or other. But I didn't have the time to do this stuff. Rachel bought lots of magazines and kept showing me pictures of how she wanted it to be: this was the colour she wanted, and this was the wallpaper, and this was the furniture, and I thought, *Shit, this is going to cost an arm and a leg.* We agreed what needed doing, and I stumped up the money and we got it done. It looked great, and Rachel seemed to be happy while she was planning what she wanted, and when I was organising it and it was getting done. And then, when it was done, she seemed pleased for a while, and all her friends came round and had coffee mornings.

'Then she seemed to sink back into not feeling happy or fulfilled, and the hours I was working got even longer, and a lot of weekends were full of reading stuff ready for the following week. We got talking about the kids' future. James was coming up to ten, I think, and Jennifer was nearly nine, and my parents suggested it would be good if James went to prep school – and said they would pay for it. I thought it was a lot of money, but it would make life easier. The local school was OK, but going to prep school would be better for him. Rachel was against it, but eventually she gave in and James started. He found it hard to adjust, but he's a good boy and it meant he could start playing proper sports, like rugby, and cricket in the summer. He soon got into the swing of things.

'Jennifer was about nine and we wondered whether she may go to prep school, too. My parents thought it would be good if they both went to boarding school, as that would free up our time and give them a better start in life. They talked about West Dene, which is where I went. Once again Rachel was against it, and eventually she gave in, but we had lots of arguments about it. So that was the plan for the kids' schooling, when the time came, and life went on. We still didn't have much time together, and sex...'

Here I paused. It felt strange talking about this stuff to two strangers.

Neil and Maria had been listening closely throughout, and asking occasional questions; but now Neil looked at me and said, 'It's really important we talk about sex and intimacy. What we want to do is create a safe space in which you both feel free to talk about the really important things in your lives. We have worked with hundreds of clients, and there is nothing you could say that would shock us or surprise us because we have heard some amazing stories, and some really sad stories. What is really important, right now, is to hear your story.'

I took a breath and carried on. 'Sex had been off the agenda for a long time. I tried to get Rachel interested on Sunday mornings –

and I still do – but she often turned over or said something like she was tired, or had the children to think about. That...well, that still happens sometimes. Our sex life is a bit of a wasteland.'

'Thank you for telling us that,' Neil said. 'We will come back to this, because it's clearly important to you.'

I nodded, not sure what I thought about that.

'So,' I continued, 'life carried on. I was working hard, with no time to enjoy myself. Rachel seemed a bit happier, but I would still get home to an untidy house, a grumpy wife, and children who didn't seem grateful. My only escape was rugby, and sometimes that would extend to the afternoon, and maybe even the evening, and I started to wonder how long I could keep this life up, and why I was doing it. To bring you up to the present, people at work started picking up that I was stressed and not in a good place. Rachel and I talked about it, and Rachel said we needed to get away, so she booked a holiday in Grenada, which I thought we couldn't really afford but I went along with it and paid for it.

'We got to this lovely place, and I was all ready for two weeks of relaxing in the sunshine and chilling out. But Rachel met up with a couple and she got talking to them – to Olivia and Richard – and they said they had been clients of yours ten years ago. They got us interested in their story, and what they had achieved as a result, and I guess that's why we are here now. Some of the time on holiday was good; other times a real rollercoaster ride. We made love a few times – well, had a few 'encounters' – and it was OK sometimes and difficult other times. We seemed to be out of sync, wanting different things at different times and not really able to get back in sync again. We got back home about a week ago, and here we are now, and that is my story to date.'

Rachel had been listening intently the whole time I had been talking and, at times, looked shocked and a bit upset. But she stayed quiet and didn't interrupt.

Neil and Maria thanked me, and then Rachel started telling her story, and it was strange listening to it, because it seemed a different story to my story at times. Quite a few times I wanted to interrupt and say, No that's not right, you've got it wrong! But when I looked like I was about to speak either Neil or Maria looked at me and made me remember I had agreed I would keep quiet and allow Rachel to tell her story. I admit I was quite shocked to hear some of her memories.

Then we got on to our past, and what was significant, and I told the story about how I had been an only child and how my parents were quite aloof.

'My father, Ken, was quite a stern figure. He was a lawyer and a partner in a big law firm. We lived in a big house in Sunningdale, and he would go off to work and I wouldn't see much of him in the evenings. At weekends he was there some of the time, but didn't really seem to know what to do with me. My mother, Pip, was lovely, and she was big in the local church and was a very huggy sort of woman. I went away to boarding school, to West Dene, when I was quite young, and that was where I learnt to play rugby and do proper boy things. I wasn't the brightest boy at school, but I got enough A levels to go to university. My father wanted me to go to Cambridge, where he had been, but I didn't do well enough to get into Cambridge so I went to Warwick, which was OK, but I felt the disappointment from my father. I had a good time at university. The law stuff was a bit boring; but the rugby and drinking and partying made up for it. Then I met Rachel, and then I was on track for...' I looked at Rachel. 'And that is my story.'

Rachel leant across the settee and squeezed my knee and whispered, 'Thank you.'

Neil and Maria thanked me too, and then asked what outcome we both wanted from the sessions. I said the outcome I wanted, as I had put on my form, was to have a good, loving relationship, to feel valued, and to have a good sex life. I also said I needed Rachel to understand the pressures I was under, and for her to express gratitude for what I did because I felt unvalued. I felt I was working really hard and not getting anything in return.

Neil said there was one more exercise they were going to do with us that day. They handed us each a big drawing book and a whole bunch of felt tips and crayons. He said he would like us to draw a picture of life as it was right now, and then draw a different picture of life as we would like it to be in the future. I thought this was a bit silly, and said I couldn't draw, and Neil laughed and said most people told them that, but I could do it in a way that felt right to me.

As I started drawing, I felt an intense pressure and anger coming from my head down through my arms, through my fingers, into the pen, and onto the paper. The picture I drew was of a big house with Rachel and three children and the dog in one group, and me some distance away, the other side of the house. I also included a big office building in London, and a trainline connecting me to that faraway place. That was it. I am useless at drawing, but there it was in front of me. I didn't have a smile on my face. Rachel, the kids and the dog looked a bit happier, and it made me question again what on earth this was all about.

I then turned the page and drew a different picture of life as I would like it to be. It was the same house, and work was still there, but the trainline had gone, so I wasn't sure how I was going to get there. I was standing next to Rachel and the kids, and there was a smart car on the drive – I'd always fancied a silver, convertible Porsche. I drew a sun and an island, because I thought it would be lovely to go on regular holidays somewhere. The picture was certainly different, and it felt much better.

And that was it. The three-and-a-half hours had gone in a flash, and I had been listened to, and had expressed stuff, but I was not sure what I had learnt.

Neil and Maria gave us some homework to do, and handed us folders with our names on which had different exercises in them. I decided I would read them through properly when I got home, because I'd tuned out after drawing the pictures.

They asked us to share one thing we would take away from

today. I thought about it and said it had been great to talk about things I hadn't talked about for far too many years. I said I felt listened to, that even Rachel was listening to me, and that I was happy we hadn't argued.

Eighteen years together, and now we could listen – albeit in the company of strangers. It felt good.

Chapter 28: The First Session - Rachel

When John came and told me he had booked a session to see Neil and Maria I was really surprised. I thought I would have to push him, or be the one to actually book it in the first place. I thought, *Wow, that is a big step. This isn't the John I know.* I got an email with forms to fill in, and questionnaires about the past, about what we wanted, and a timeline about significant things in our lives. They were really interesting questions, asking me to rate out of ten aspects of our life, about what we agree on, what we disagree on, family, sex and various other things. I emailed them back and looked forward, but with some apprehension, to our first session.

I'd had counselling before, which I hadn't told John about, to deal with my unhappiness after Rowena was born, and my life in general, which didn't feel fulfilling. I saw two different counsellors, and they both listened but didn't really offer any opinions. I got the sense that I could spend the rest of my life going there and off-loading about the bad things, and that was quite depressing. What I really needed was somebody to give me some guidance, somebody to tell me what I could do differently. I guess I also hoped somebody would wave a magic wand and make John a loving, fun husband.

We drove down. I watched the countryside go past, wishing I could listen to some of my favourite music. John put on some opera, and I asked him if he could turn it off as I can't bear it. I wanted to hear some good rock music, which would take me to a different place, but I knew John wouldn't like that. After a few failed attempts at finding music that both of us would enjoy, we settled down to a quiet and slightly tense journey.

Previous counsellors I had been to operated from their spare bedroom, and it had felt a bit strange going into somebody's house and seeing how they lived, feeling partly jealous and partly judgemental. I was a bit surprised when we drew up outside an office building and went in through a spacious lobby and up a big sweeping staircase. Two people were waiting at the top: Neil and Maria. Neil was an older man with a beard and, how shall I put it politely, he was stocky, but he looked wise and understanding. Maria was younger and looked calm and very capable – somebody I could talk to about anything. They showed us into a lovely big, light room with lots of shelves holding an interesting collection of books on relationships and sex and people and all sorts of stuff. I looked for titles I recognised, wishing I could take some out and sit there, flicking through.

They made us drinks – peppermint tea for me, and fresh coffee for John – and we sat down, John one end of the settee and me at the other. It felt safer that way. I didn't want to be so close to him that I had to touch him. They explained the way this would work, and that this session was about understanding how we had both got to where we are right now. They said they would listen, and ask questions if necessary, but without any judgement. They also explained it was important for us to listen to each other, as inevitably we would have two different perspectives on what had happened, and it was important we understood that even if we thought they were wrong, they weren't wrong, it was just how they saw things.

We had the slightly embarrassing 'Well, who's going to go first?' question, and John went first. And then it was my turn.

'I was at a noisy, dark rugby club party, with beer on the floor – so much beer it was sticky – and standing near a table with damp French sticks, big chunks of tasteless yellow stuff which was supposed to be cheese, and a big tub of margarine. There were plastic knives to try and assemble all this into sandwiches. There were also a few bottles of warm wine, but mainly beer.

'I had been invited along by a friend who said it might be

fun, and that "you never know who you might meet." I'd been really upset. I'd had a couple of relationships at university but been dumped. I saw John looking at me across the room. He was tall, and quite good-looking. He looked like a rugby player, and was probably half-pissed, but was able to stand up, which was pretty good given the state of the other people in the room. He came over to me and gave me the cheesy chat-up line – I can't even remember what it was – and I laughed and gave a stupid response. He asked a few questions, and we got chatting, and I felt safe with him. We had a bit of a lurch around the dancefloor and we ended up walking back together.

'The halls he lived in were some distance from mine, but somehow we ended up at his. His room was messy, and had some strange posters on the wall. But there were lots of thick books piled up on the bookshelf – law stuff, I guessed. He went and made me some tea, and when he came back he leant over and gave me a kiss, which felt nice. I put down the tea and held him and kissed him back. That was a really long kiss, and I just sank into it. One thing led to another and we made love, which was a bit hurried and fumbly, but it was OK.

'Then we ended up living in the same place together, in the same room. There wasn't much space. John was in his last year, and I was in my second year, and we went to parties and some concerts together, but our taste in music was very different. He didn't really like rock music, which I thought was unusual for a rugby player, but that was him. We had some shared friends. John graduated and went off down to London and lived with a friend. He came back some weekends and we had a good time together. I felt in a safe place with him. Then I graduated, and got a great job with Unilever on their management development scheme and felt really proud.

'John was training as a solicitor in London, and my work was based in London, so we talked about moving in together. We found a really lovely flat in Putney in a big old Victorian house. We didn't have much money, so we got furniture from junk shops, and I spent some time trying to make it look nice in between working hard and doing lots of training. I got a job as trainee brand manager of a soap brand, which I found exciting. I liked working in marketing.

'We had a group of friends who lived nearby, and we would go out drinking and eating and partying at weekends. Life seemed pretty good. I got promoted, and got really excited about future prospects. I remember thinking, *Wow, this is it, senior brand manager on soap, could there be anything better*! And I got lots of free samples. Things were OK between John and me, but the sex was fading as we were both tired. And the time spent having fun together faded as well.

'One weekend I went to spend time with my mother, as John was away on a rugby tour, and she told me something that was a real shock. She had discovered, some years ago, that my father had had an affair with his secretary, which lasted ten years. They hadn't really talked about it, though, so it had never been resolved. And she told me how a wall had gone up between them, but they were married and had to make it work and couldn't tell anyone about it. That changed things for me, with my father. I didn't really want to have anything to do with him from that moment on, but he was still in my life. I felt emotionally disconnected from him, but I still wanted him to be there for me.

'Then John and I went away for the weekend and I got pregnant, and that was a real shock, because I had been on the pill as I didn't want to get pregnant. It was too soon. Yes, I wanted children, but it wasn't the right time. When I found out I was uncertain what to do, and I was uncertain what to say to John. But I talked to him and he was good about it. He asked me what I wanted to do, and said he would support me in that. He also said his parents would be really upset if I had an abortion and I thought, *What have his parents got to do with it?*

'We decided we would have the baby, but that we needed to get married first. I was due to give birth in a few months so we arranged a quick register office wedding. We didn't tell our parents about it, just did it in Putney; and didn't push the boat out, just invited a few friends for drinks and snacks at the pub later. John arranged a quick holiday in Paris, where I'd said I always wanted to go. The wedding was functional. It wasn't a big church wedding, which my parents would have loved, and my sister and brother would have liked to come to. But the sight of me with an obvious bump coming down the aisle would have really upset my parents. They would have found it hard to cope with that, which was why we chose to get married sooner in the registry office.

'We went off to Paris and had a lovely couple of days. The weather was good, and we walked a bit, and went to the Louvre – which I suppose everyone who goes to Paris does – and we fought our way through the throngs of Japanese tourists to see the Mona Lisa. I thought, *Oh well, I can tick that off my list. Let's go somewhere more interesting.* We walked to somewhere called the Orangerie, which has Monet pictures in it. We walked down the stairs into this huge horseshoe-shaped room in the basement, and wow, there was the picture with the water lilies. I felt I was floating in the pond in Giverny, and it was such a magical moment. I felt immersed in the picture. Not just staring at a small rectangle from a distance, but actually in the picture. That was a very memorable moment for me, and John was there, and I held his hand and squeezed it, and I think he was experiencing something similar. Then we walked on through the gardens and enjoyed eating great food, although it was rather expensive. I wasn't drinking alcohol because of being pregnant.

'We got back to London, back to the flat. A couple of months later James was born. So it was off to Charing Cross Hospital. The birth was fairly easy. John didn't make it, though, and I felt pissed off that he'd put his clients before the birth of his first child. But he arrived full of excuses, and when he held James it was a big moment, and usually an emotional moment...

'I got back home and my mother came to help out, and that was difficult. I felt she was intruding into our life, and my life, and getting between me and the baby. And she kept telling me what to do. James was a good baby, but I felt a bit disconnected from him. And John went back to work and I kept telling him I couldn't cope with my mother being there, and could he ask her to go. And John would keep saying, "She's your mother. I can't ask her to go. Can you?" So, after a week, I summoned up the courage to thank her for helping, but that it would be good if we could have some time on our own. She looked disappointed, and went off in a bit of a huff.

'Then there was just John and me looking after James. I was on six months maternity leave, but was missing work. John was enthusiastic about doing stuff with James, but it was almost as if he couldn't wait for him to grow up so that he could play rugby and do other boy stuff together, and so on. Things like changing nappies, or bathing him, John couldn't really do, so I had to do all that stuff.

'I missed the intellectual challenge of work, and although selling soap doesn't exactly sound intellectual, I was working with other enthusiastic, bright people who had interesting lives to talk about, and now all I did was talk to myself and goo-goo language to James. None of our friends had children yet, so I was the first, so I didn't really fit into the going out and getting pissed thing that we had been into before.

'I felt very lonely, and John started to work longer and longer hours. And we realised our flat really wasn't big enough, and wasn't practical, so we started looking for somewhere else to live. We found a three-bedroomed house in Twickenham, which needed some work done to it. John refused to let me use tradesmen, and insisted on trying to do it all himself...but I think he might admit now that he's not the world's best DIY man. I remember the pile of plaster on the floor, which was probably the highlight of his attempts, but there had been many others: bookshelves which fell off the walls, taps that leaked. Sorry, John, your skills definitely lie elsewhere!

'Eventually we got the house OK, and James was actually a lovely baby. He was happy, and he was growing fast. I found some new friends in Twickenham, and then we talked about having another baby, and it seemed a good time to start trying for another.

People say try for another baby, but I'm not quite sure what you need to try, other than having sex, and that had become pretty infrequent and not great.

'Some of my friends invited me to join the NCT and talk about bringing up happy, healthy babies, and they told me it was much better if babies could be born in a home environment, so I started planning the next baby, whenever they might appear. Then Jennifer was conceived, and I was looking forward to a home birth, and everything was arranged. The midwife came just as I was starting to have contractions, and told me something wasn't quite right, and that she needed to get me into hospital – and that was a scary, scary moment. The ambulance came and off we went, with the sirens blaring. I was wheeled into a maternity ward, and they took various readings and soundings, and whisked me straight into surgery. They said I needed a caesarean because it was a breach birth.

'I didn't know much about what happened after that, but Jennifer was born, crying from the first moment. She wasn't happy, and I wasn't happy, and it felt like that line in Macbeth about the child "from the mother's womb being untimely ripped" and not "naturally" born. For a long time I felt she wasn't my baby, and that something had been taken from me, and John wasn't particularly engaged. He didn't cope well with this baby, who'd had a difficult birth and was unhappy and cried a lot. She didn't want to be breastfed, either, so I felt my life with the NCT had a marked card now: not a natural birth and not breastfeeding. I felt shunned by them. Jennifer didn't sleep very well, and I was absolutely exhausted. I had James to look after too, and John was a reluctant father and didn't help out at night when she woke up. He didn't really understand how bad it was for me. I felt a failure, and John responded by working even longer hours.

'My parents came around some of the time and gave a bit of help. But I felt my mother had never got over the fact I had asked her to leave a week after James was born; and my father had never had anything to do with my upbringing, or my sister or brother, so he wasn't much use. John's parents came over, too. They were very generous with the cheque book, but not really there emotionally for me. I felt a real failure, and I had given up work completely because I had two children to look after now, and my career and my bright hopes of conquering the world of clean people had disappeared. I had a husband I felt disconnected from, and didn't see very much.

'I'd asked John if we could go away, because I was finding it hard to cope, so we went to New York. We had, for the first time in a long, long time, a magical three days, and we made love frequently. It was so good, and John was kind and caring. I didn't want the weekend to end, and thought, *I'm back in love again!*

'A couple of months later I found out I was pregnant. We talked about what we should do, and I was reluctant to keep it, because the next baby would definitely be the end of my career, but John wanted another child, because he couldn't face telling his parents we'd had an abortion... We agreed we would have the baby, and Rowena was born and the birth went OK. It was in hospital because of my previous history, but it was a gentle birth, and I looked up and there was John holding Rowena – and that was a big surprise. I could see tears in his eyes, and it was the first time he'd looked like he was really connected with any of our three children. I held Rowena and she was lovely. She really felt part of me, and I thought, *There is hope for John and me. We have a new baby together. I hope we can get to a really good place.*

Then we got back home, and John was back into his work rhythm, and James was at nursery. He was a good boy, and growing up fast, and he was fun to have around. Jennifer was still very difficult. She was not sleeping well, wetting the bed, and had lots of tantrums. And it seems horrible to say, but...I really didn't like her. Rowena irritated Jennifer, and Jennifer was mean to her. She felt her place was the baby of the family, and not in the middle. James, bless him, was protective of Rowena. He loved her, and would rock her in the pram and push her around. He was a lovely older brother.

'I needed some help and Paula, my younger sister, came to stay.

We hadn't been that close, and there was quite an age gap between us, but she'd had a relationship breakdown and was looking for some security, and she was also between jobs. But, actually, it was lovely having her around, having somebody who I could talk to, somebody I could share stuff with. I felt in tune with her.

'It was a bit odd when John came home, and Paula was there, and I think he felt a bit separate from us. She stayed for about six months, and then she started work again, which took her to a different part of the country. She also had a new man in her life. It was good to see her moving on, but now it was John and me and three children again, and the final realisation that my career was over. I'd had a discussion with my boss about the future, and he said I'd had all the maternity leave I was entitled to and would I come back to work – and that they'd love to have me back. Sadly, I had to say no, because how would I cope? John was away during the day, and there was nobody to look after three children. I didn't want to stick Jennifer in nursery, even if they would have her, and Rowena was much too young. My boss said, "When they're older come and talk to us." He then said, again, that they would love to have me back. But I knew their world would have moved on by then.

'I felt depressed, I felt sad, and I felt lonely. I went to see my doctor, who I don't see very often, and he said he had some pills which would help, and wrote out a prescription for something called Fluoxetine; but when I looked up the side effects on the internet, there was no way I was going to take them. They were not going to solve my problems. I'd have to sort them out myself. I cried and cried, and threw the pills in the bin. *Is this what my life is going to be?* I thought. *Where is my husband? Where is he in this?*

'I phoned the Samaritans and a quiet, calm voice answered. The man listened, but I don't think he really understood what I was going through. All he could really offer was platitudes. He'd never had a baby, never mind three, and wasn't married to what felt like an absent father. I talked for about half an hour, and felt better for having off-loaded, but it wasn't good enough.

'I packed the children in the car and drove down to see my mother in Bournemouth. She was surprised to see me, and we sat in the garden and talked. But she kept getting up and watering the plants and I said, "Please, Mum, I need to talk to you, can you just sit still and listen?" She listened for a while, when I was talking about how unhappy I was with John and how he wasn't being supportive, and then she got up again and started watering the bloody plants...and I shouted at her, "Please, I need to talk to you!" but she carried on, going back every few minutes to fill up this tiny watering can from the garden tap. I felt like that bloody garden was more important than me; that she seemed to spend most of her life poking about out there, and watering was more important than her daughter. Eventually, she put down the watering can and said, "John is a good man. You just need to be grateful for what you have, and you need to make it work." And with that she turned round and started watering the bloody plants again.

'I went to get the children from inside, where they had been playing. Rowena was fast asleep in her travel cot. I put them in the car and drove off. I felt really sad that my mother wasn't able to help me, but I realised this was something that only I could fix, and I needed to stop feeling sorry for myself.

'I got back home and decided I needed to exercise and get fit, and maybe then I would feel better. I joined the local gym and arranged for Jennifer and Rowena to stay in the creche. I made a few friends while I was there – well, a few of the gym bunnies on the treadmills – and I started to get into the local mother scene.

'Life went on. James went to full-time school, and a year later Jennifer started school, and I had more time to myself. Rowena was growing up a bit and the disturbed nights started to reduce. Then John got promoted, further up the ladder he had been climbing, to being a partner of the firm, and finally having his name on the notepaper. He was not made an equity partner, so he didn't get a big share of the good times, but at least he got a bigger salary.

'We decided to buy a bigger house. We looked in Twickenham, and a bit further away, and thought it would be good to live somewhere where there was less noise and more space. We also looked at schools for the children to go to. We found a great house in East Horsley, and John's parents helped out, because it was much more than we could afford. They said John would get all the money when they died, anyway, so why not enjoy it now? I was so grateful for that, but I wanted to make it feel like our house, so I spent a lot of time and effort searching for stuff we would both like. I arranged for a new kitchen to be installed, for all the decorating to be done, and for a beautiful conservatory. John wasn't really interested. He went off to work early in the morning and came back even later at night.

'We got the children into schools. Rowena loved it. Jennifer was becoming an easier child to be around, and James was lovely, but somehow it still didn't feel enough, because at the weekends John would go off to his rugby, sometimes coming back pissed, we rarely did much together, and the evenings were hopeless. John would come home from work, eat the dinner I had cooked, and go to bed. There was no intimacy; no connection at all really.

'We had a big argument about James going to prep school. I wanted him to go to the local school, which was really good. We also argued about the future, and how he wanted James and Jennifer to go to the school he had gone to – a boarding school. I was horrified at the prospect of my children going to boarding school, and being away from me; but John was adamant that was what was going to happen, and I just didn't have the power to say no.

'Some of my friends at the gym had relationship problems, and we talked about our unhappiness. But knowing I wasn't alone didn't actually help. I felt like I was on a slow, downward slope. I felt trapped. And I couldn't talk to John about how I felt. Every day felt like Groundhog Day. What was my purpose in life?'

I could tell John was surprised by some of the things I'd said, and Maria and Neil were listening intently. The questions they asked were really helpful, and the silence was also really helpful, letting me open up. When I'd heard John's story about his life, initially I felt quite angry that he really didn't understand what my life was like; but slowly I began to get where he was, and see the misunderstandings between the two of us. I really hoped he had been able to see how my life was now, and that he'd understand.

Then I talked about my earlier life, which was pretty uneventful.

'I had a really busy father, who never expressed his emotions. His measure of happiness was being successful, and I was never particularly praised by him or my mother. I did well at school, though, and my parents seemed OK with that. My father wanted me to become an accountant, because that was what he was; but that was something I absolutely refused to do, and he didn't like the fact I wasn't following the path he had "laid down for me".

'As I was growing up, I enjoyed rock music and sailing, and I had a few boyfriends. My older brother, Victor, is forty-five and, surprise, surprise, is a chartered accountant. He lives in Manchester. He was married to a woman for twenty years who I thought was awful, but he broke up with her, and that was painful for him. He'd had an affair, though, and that's why the marriage ended. I felt angry with him for betraying her, even though it was the wrong marriage for him.

'My younger sister Paula was the apple of my parents' eyes when she was born – a surprise arrival late in life for my mother – and she got all the things I never got, like a proper bike rather than a bike which was too big for her. She got new clothes and she got birthday parties and birthday presents. I guess my father was better off then, but she seemed to get more of his time, too, and certainly more of my mother's time and attention. Anyway, I'm pretty close to her now, and she's been good to me. She hasn't really made her mark in life, though.'

When I heard John talk about his background, and how his parents were with him, I heard him say things he had never said before. I had never really understood the lonely, only child that he was. And I had never really understood all the emotions he had repressed, because he had never let me see them. It sent shivers down my spine, hearing those secrets come out, and seeing John be vulnerable. I just wanted to hold him and make it all better.

Our first session came to an end. We were given homework to do, and asked what we had got from the first session. I said I had got so much from it just by being listened to properly, and being able to express how I felt, and also seeing John express himself and his emotions. It was as if something much more solid than a curtain had been lifted; it was like a portcullis had been raised, and it made me wonder whether there was hope, whether the John I had married all those years ago was actually a much more vulnerable person than I had thought.

As we said our goodbyes, I found myself looking forward to our next session.

Chapter 29: In Between - Rachel

John was quiet on the way home, and I was reflective as well. I reached out once to hold his hand and he took his off the wheel and held it. I sensed something was a little bit different between us.

We'd told my parents, who were babysitting, that we'd been going out to dinner with old friends, and they asked about them when we got home, but I'd brushed them off and not gone into too much detail because I knew I would have to make up lies if I did. The next day they drove back down to Bournemouth, because my mother had her garden to look after – her obsession. My father, he was her assistant. The two of them somehow coped with each other, I think because they had shared interests but separate hobbies too. She had her garden, obviously, and he had his Probus Club and would go to lunches with other retired business people, which he seemed to enjoy, which was good.

The next few days passed in a humdrum of usual routines, with John off to work early and James and Jennifer arguing in the car on the way to school, and Rowena off in her dream world. Home-time would involve James playing FIFA or Call of Duty, scoring goals or killing people in his weird virtual reality world, and Jennifer living in Snapchat world, or whichever social media app was her current favourite. Rowena and me were the only ones who seemed to have any fun, talking and taking Woody for walks. Jennifer did bake some cakes, though, which were delicious – but guess who always had to clear the mess up in the kitchen...

It felt like John and I were a bit closer, but he still wanted sex at the weekends, which I didn't. I said I wanted to 'make love' not have sex, which John seemed to not like. I did my homework and found it interesting. I tried to engage John in it a few times, but he said he was busy and would do his on the Wednesday night before our next appointment. He did do it, and I was pleasantly surprised I didn't have to force him. Part of my homework was free writing, and a whole heap of different stuff came up about my career, which went up in smoke, about my parents, and my frustration that my mother wouldn't listen or really help me in my time of need. I also wrote about my father and feeling, not a direct disapproval, but certainly a lack of encouragement from him when I was growing up. I wrote about feeling in limbo, with no career, and the children not needing me as much, and my sense of disconnection, which sometimes felt more like a deep unhappiness.

Then, as instructed in the homework notes, I took what I had written and burnt it. I put the sheets of paper on a slab on the patio, put a few stones around it and set fire to it, and just sat there watching it burn. As it turned to ashes I cried a few tears of release, and hope, and studied the ashes left behind that the rain would wash away, and that felt good, and natural.

The evening before our second appointment, John surprised me when he told me he'd taken the day off work. I had already arranged to see some people that morning, but I could see he was a bit disappointed. Why hadn't he told me sooner? Anyway, we drove down and had a late lunch in a pub on the quay and looked at the boats. I was thinking about how lovely it would be to have a boat and just head off over the horizon to a new and different life. I mentioned that to John, and he said, 'I don't like sailing, remember?' This time, however, I asked him why, and he told me about an experience he had when he was very young, where he had fallen out and almost drowned. He had never told me about that before? What else would I find out about this man, my husband, who I had been with for the last eighteen years?

Chapter 30: In Between - John

I left feeling OK, and glad I had been able to say a lot of important things – for me. I also felt that Rachel had been listening and, yes, what she had said was different to me, but it helped me understand her perspective. I was really hopeful that these sessions would help get Rachel back to the place she needed to be; there was also a little seed growing within me about what life I really wanted. I reflected on that picture of us all together – the big house, the Porsche on the drive, and work – and wondered how that would work, because it was still me who paid for all this stuff. Maybe I needed to think about that... Rachel was quiet on the way back, but happyish.

We hadn't told Rachel's parents where we were going, because I didn't want to get them involved. They stayed the night in the guest room and I went off to work early the next morning...same train, same seat, same people. But this time I felt a sense that I was on a journey to something else, which could hopefully be better.

Rachel reminded me about our homework a few days later, but I was so busy and told her I would do it before our next session. When she reminded me again I thought, *Shit, I forgot all about that.*

I got my folder. There was a quiz called Emotional History, which I filled in, and that seemed to be quite easy. There was also something called Free Writing, which said something like "Take some time where you are not going to be interrupted and write non-stop for about fifteen minutes. At the end of that fifteen minutes, take a break for a few minutes, and then come back and read through what you have written to see what themes there are. When you have absorbed what you have written, take it and burn it somewhere safely." I thought, *Wow, this is a bit weird, but let's give it a go...* So, when the kids were in bed, I told Rachel I was going to be about half an hour or so, and not to interrupt me, and I sat down in my study and started writing. It was strange writing non-stop, because I wanted to keep stopping to read through what I had written, to see if it made any sense, but the words began to shape up, sentences started to flow, and the fifteen minutes passed very quickly.

At the end of that fifteen minutes I stopped, went and made some coffee, and came back and read through what I had written. It was quite sad reading it through. There was a load of stuff about working too hard, not feeling valued, not enough sex, what was the point of it all, the children didn't really know me, and Rachel and me were still not good, etc. I felt quite depressed reading it, so I took the paper and screwed it up, went outside to the barbeque and set fire to it, and just stood there watching it. It was a clear night, with lots of stars, and I felt a sense of relief having got this stuff out, and watched the orange sparks float up into the sky.

When I went back inside, Rachel asked me what I had been doing, and I told her I had just been doing one of the exercises. She was pleased and asked me if I was looking forward to tomorrow, our next session. I said I didn't really know, but that I'd taken the day off so we could leave early and not rush. Rachel said she still had to get the children to school, and had an appointment at the gym and wouldn't be able to leave until later. I felt a bit disappointed, but decided to do some work from home. It would be great not having to get on the train to go into work.

It was a novelty having breakfast with the kids before they went off to school. And then Rachel packed her gym bag and off she went, and I was left in the house on my own. It was the first time I had been on my own in the house for a long time, and I just walked around from room to room thinking, *Where am I in this house? What is there that matters to me?* The only place I could really find anything that was just mine was in my study: a few old pictures, a few things that I had picked up on my travels. The rest of the house was about the kids and about Rachel, although there were a few wedding photos about. I felt like a stranger here.

Rachel came back, looking happy, and we got in the car and headed down to Lymington. We had lunch together in a lovely pub on the quay, and Rachel seemed relaxed and we talked about the kids, what a sunny day it was, about the boats that were out there. Rachel said how great it would be to go sailing a long distance, across the oceans. I shuddered a bit, because the only time I tried sailing I fell in and almost drowned.

When people talk, listen completely.
Most people never listen.

– Ernest Hemingway

Chapter 31: The Second Session

COMMUNICATION - John

I walked into the room, still not quite sure what to expect. I had my folder with me, with the work I had done, so at least felt I might get a gold star for doing that. We were welcomed again, and offered drinks, and we sat in the same place. I was not sure if I was imagining it, but Rachel felt slightly closer to me.

First of all we were asked what had happened between the last session and now. Rachel went first, and talked about what had happened for her, and I was a bit surprised that her account seemed so different from mine. But I was beginning to understand what that meant.

I talked about my two weeks; about work being almost overwhelming; about nothing much changing. I said that maybe we'd had fewer arguments, but no sex, and were in the same old pattern of me working and Rachel doing her stuff and the kids doing their stuff. I also said I'd been thinking about the future and wondering what this life was all about, and that I didn't have any answers yet, but the thoughts were coming.

We were asked about the homework, and I talked about the writing I had done and how it had made me think. Neil said I might find it helpful to repeat this exercise with thoughts about the future, as it was a great way of getting out of your head, and all that was buzzing around in our subconsciousness.

Then we talked about the quiz on the past, and how comfortable we were with various aspects, and looked at our respective scores. I scored pretty low on pride and a sense of accomplishment, maybe because my father was a bit aloof and I don't really remember him ever giving me any praise. My mum tried, but she was in a different place. The second score, on how comfortable I was with love and affection, reflected once again on my relationship with my dad, and had always been something I'd been striving for but never yet received. I scored really low on that. Rachel's was higher, as both her parents were far more affectionate.

The third question was about anger. I'd never heard my parents argue, maybe because they didn't have anything to argue about; or maybe they just did it behind closed doors. Even so, anger was something I felt uncomfortable with, whereas Rachel was a bit different. Her parents did have disagreements, and they did get angry with each other, but it soon dissipated.

The fourth question was about sadness. There were a few times in my past where I'd felt sad but couldn't really express it. I remember when I was young, about four or five years old, something really upset me and I started crying, and I got a very stern rebuke from my father. 'Real men don't cry,' he said. From that point on, whatever sadness I felt was bottled up within me.

Last of all was how comfortable I was with fear. That was a strange thing. I have a memory from the past, when the GPO man – what they called BT back then – was putting a telephone cable in the house, up in the attic, and he fell through the ceiling and into my bedroom. For weeks there was a big hole in my ceiling, and I had nightmares every night about a monster from up above coming into my bedroom. Every night I woke up screaming, and every night my father would come into my room and, in quite a stern voice, ask me what was wrong. When I told him he would tell me not to be stupid, that there was nothing up there, and to go back to sleep.

We then went through the scores, and Neil and Maria highlighted the impact our past had had on us; first of all because of the differences between the two of us, and secondly because those emotions of pride, love, anger, sadness and fear were formed at a fairly early age, and if they hadn't been well formed they often cause us problems in the future.

I found this interesting. It explained why, maybe, I bottled things up and didn't express my thoughts. It definitely gave me something to think about.

Then we were asked if we had any questions, and if there weren't any specific questions, what we would like to have happen in that session. Rachel expressed her needs and wants, and I said I was happy to see what happened.

Neil and Maria then explained that this session was going to focus on communication, as communication was a key part of the thing called The Relationship Paradigm, which was something they would explain as the sessions went on.

They said some interesting things. First of all that we can never not communicate; that even when we are saying nothing, there is communication. Silence is communication; a look is communication; the lack of a look or looking away is communication. We never switch off from communicating.

The second thing they said that got me thinking was that the meaning of any communication is the message that is received. We may think we are saying something very clearly, but what is critical is what the other person is actually hearing. I found that so interesting that I started making notes. Neil also said, 'There is no reality, there is only perception.' I tried to think of ways to disprove that, but I wasn't able to.

The last thought, which we most definitely hadn't sorted out, and which made life so hard, were the things that were unsaid. This made me think about all the things I had never said to Rachel, things that had just festered. For instance, the lack of frequent sex – I had never actually expressed my true feelings to her about that. So many nights of going to bed, being next to her, wanting to have sex but not getting any indication from her that was a possibility, and just going to sleep feeling frustrated, rejected and disconnected. Then waking up the next morning wondering how she would respond, not on work days, but at the weekends or on holiday. Just lying there watching her sleeping, reaching out and touching her, and having her turn to me and say it's too early and turn her back again. Those moments made me feel sad, rejected, and unimportant.

My thoughts drifted off into a rather gloomy place, and I was brought back into the moment by Neil explaining we were going to do an exercise where we would to talk to each other about something which was important in our lives, something which hadn't been resolved. He said it could be a different thing for each of us, and we would both be able to talk. The structure we would use, he said, was something called Interactive Listening. He explained this meant we would choose a subject, and we would each take it in turns, for about fifteen minutes. The one listening would put all their attention on their partner, staying curious about what was actually being said, but digging all the time for feelings because, as Neil expressed, this wasn't about the stuff, this was about the feelings: What was this like for you? How did you feel about this? What was the worst thing about this for you? etc.

This perhaps sounds a bit sad, and difficult, but it was an exercise that meant your partner felt less alone, and that you really got to where they were at. It also meant that even if you thought they were in the wrong, you could prove you were on their side, that you were not the enemy. They explained that we must not rush to problem-solve; that this was all about the other person being able to express how they were feeling about the subject. This made me smile, as it is a typical male trait to rush in and try to solve a problem.

We were encouraged to ask for clarification if we did not

understand a point made, and to ask questions such as: Are you just venting the issue or do you want help? Do you want me just to listen right now, or do you want me to think how to help you? for example. At the end, we were instructed to provide validation of the subject raised, endorsing what our partner had said by saying, 'It makes sense to me that you would feel that way, and have these feelings, because...' This sounded like an interesting structure, and I was curious to see what subject Rachel would choose to talk about.

I thought about what I would like to talk about. The sex thing was a bit too intimate, so I decided to raise the subject of the kids' schooling, because it hadn't really been resolved. Rachel had been very unhappy when we had discussed this.

Rachel said she would like to raise the subject of the burden of running the house, and instinctively I thought, *Shit, that is really not fair. I work bloody hard. What does she actually do to justify all the money I put into keeping a roof over our heads?* I could feel an argument coming, and felt it was better to get it over with.

Neil and Maria said they would coach us both, so they would interrupt at times if they felt we needed help to discuss these subjects and come to a suitable conclusion on them.

I had to bite my tongue when Rachel launched into how she felt, and at first I found it hard to listen, and wanted to interrupt and say, This really isn't fair, you have got it all wrong! I work much harder than you! All you have to do is keep the house tidy, and look after the kids. You have time to go to the gym; you have time to go to lunch. I don't have time to do that!

But then she started to talk about how she felt lonely, how she'd had a great career and had to give it up for the children, and how, with the children growing up and James going off to school soon, she felt her purpose in life was diminishing. She said how hollow and empty she felt, that she didn't feel appreciated, that nothing felt like it was 'joint' any more. We were living separate lives, she said, and the arguments we had often came out of nothing. They would start when I got back home at night and things weren't as I would like them to be, and I got angry and started shouting, and how that made her feel.

Hearing her express these feelings actually made me sad, but still made me feel it was unfair, this criticism of me. I tried to tune in to what Rachel was saying, and almost try to be in her shoes. This gave me some really useful insights into her life, and I started wondering, if I was her, how I would be feeling. I tried to imagine how it would be if she escaped every day to go off to her career, to work with colleagues and do stuff, how I would feel if she came home grumpy and expecting everything to be wonderful...

What I found really interesting was that it started to affect me. I started to feel sad for her, sad for us. Neil asked me to ask her, 'Is there anything else?' and to keep asking, 'Is there anything else?' He said to dig really deep to find out the fundamental emotions. Rachel had started with anger with me, for not doing what she wanted me to do, and ended up with sadness – sadness at her life, and sadness at our life. It seemed tragic that we had such an expensive but such a sad life, and I wondered what we could do to make it better.

Once Rachel had finished talking I was asked to validate what she had said. So I looked at her and said, 'It makes sense to me that you feel sad about my part in our home life, that I am often not there because I am working, and when I am at home I am not really present in the room, I am thinking about other stuff. You are right, I am often not there, and when I am there I am often angry about what I am not getting.'

Tears welled in Rachel's eyes, and she reached out and touched my hand and gave it a squeeze, and that felt like the most intimate moment we had had for a long, long time.

Then it was my turn, and I changed my mind. I didn't talk about the kids' schooling. I started talking about my life, my work, my daily commute up to London instead, and the huge amount of pressure with clients, with my colleagues, with the senior partners in the firm. That my life was all about going round in a hamster wheel, faster and faster, to get more clients, to do more work, to make more money for the firm so that I could get promoted to a higher level, so I could make even more money to pay the mortgage, pay the school fees – well, those we are left with after my parents pay what they offered to pay – to pay for Rachel's gym membership, PT sessions, lunches and stuff, and what did I get out of all that? I said I didn't feel valued, I didn't feel appreciated, and I didn't feel praised. I was just filling up the bank account every month for other people to drain it, and I couldn't see that ending.

Rachel was listening intently and asked me some questions. She asked me, 'How does that feel for you, doing all of that?' My first feeling was anger, and the lack of appreciation, and that it all seemed a bit pointless. Rachel kept on asking me, 'Anything else?' The words kept coming out, and I told her I felt hurt at not being appreciated, and isolated in the family. The last feeling that came out was I felt so lonely, and that really resonated. I felt a great wave coming over me. I had felt lonely for so long. I had felt lonely as a child, and unloved and unappreciated by my father. I had felt lonely at university, even with the camaraderie of the rugby club; that when we weren't on the field, or when the bar wasn't open, the loneliness was always there. I said that fleetingly, with Rachel, I had felt a connection with somebody else, a real connection, but as soon as we got back into the work cycle, and as soon as I started running frantically on the treadmill to get up the promotion ladder, and as soon as the kids arrived I was no longer important. I was only there to pay for them and their stuff.

Realising that loneliness was all through me, and so significant, tears came into my eyes and I rubbed them away quickly. Maria handed me a tissue. I had never cried in public before; I had never cried in front of any other people. It felt a very strange thing to do, but I just let the tears flow.

Rachel moved closer to me on the sofa, and put her arms around me and held me tight. In that moment, with Rachel holding me, I felt safer, I felt less lonely, and the tears came to an end. Rachel still held on to me, though, and looked me in the eyes, and I thought,

Wow, I have got to fight for this. I am going to fight for the one person in my life who has really seen me, and who I have been able to be vulnerable with, and is there for me. This is going to work. I am going to fight for it.

Rachel then said, 'Thank you, John. I didn't know how lonely you were feeling, and I am so sorry. I understand why you feel so lonely and need to be appreciated, and need to feel loved, and I thought I was trying to do that. But now I understand where that loneliness comes from, I understand what I need to do, and what we need to do to be there for each other.'

A lot happened in that session. I got in touch with things I hadn't really known were there, and it felt dangerous but also safe to do that. When we were asked at the end what it was we had taken away from the session, I said, 'Understanding Rachel's needs, but also actually understanding what has really been happening for me, so thank you.'

Neil then talked to us about our levels of trust in each other and asked us to score this out of ten. He explained this was an essential element of the paradigm, because if trust is questioned, it is the sea mist that creates uncertainty, insecurity, and a lack of clarity. I had fully trusted Rachel until I had thought there might be someone else in our marriage. Our conversations had dispelled that fear, but there was a faint lingering doubt, so I gave it a score of nine. Rachel was a bit surprised to be asked, and gave me a ten, and said she had never had any reason to doubt me.

Neil asked me what I would need to get to a ten. I said I needed to know that Rachel and I could continue being open with each other, and able to discuss what we were thinking and feeling. Maria then said we would put trust to one side for now, but would ask us again in the future if things were still OK.

We arranged another session in a couple of weeks' time, and were given some more homework to do. This included a questionnaire to do with something called the State of the Union meeting, where we would have a weekly meeting to talk about the good stuff, and about the bad stuff. Another exercise was called the Daily Blessings. Every evening, before we went to sleep, we needed to talk about three good things we had noticed that day. It didn't matter how big or small they were, we just needed to share those, to end each day in a good place.

Chapter 32: The Second Session - Rachel

It felt strangely comfortable going back to Neil and Maria's office. We sat in the same place, but slightly closer – or maybe it was my imagination. Neil and Maria asked both of us what had happened since the last session, and there was quite a lot of commonality between what we said which, in a way, was comforting. They asked what we would like to have happen in that session. John said he wasn't sure. I said I would like to get more clarity, to understand what it was we were getting wrong, and what we needed to change to make that better.

They explained that this session would focus on communication, on what we were doing to communicate with each other, and different ways of communicating better, because communication was a fundamental part of the relationship paradigm. They asked us to pick a topic to talk on, each separately, and for us to listen to each other exploring what our feelings really were about that topic. They would help guide us at times, they said, but the floor was largely ours.

So John suggested I went first, and the topic I wanted to talk about was the fact that our marriage didn't feel like a partnership, that I had the load of the house and the children and stuff to cope with, and John just went off to work and would come home and it wouldn't be good enough for him. I could sense John starting to bristle, but I ploughed on. I explained how my career had ended, I was a mother to three children, one of whom was very difficult, that James was in his own world and would soon be leaving to go to boarding school, and Rowena was delightful, but I was there, in a lovely house, with a few friends, but no real purpose. I said how

John would go to work, come home and not be appreciative of everything I did to make it a lovely home, and how he would spend his weekends with his rugby mates, getting drunk, and coming home expecting dinner on the table, and how we didn't really do much together.

Then Neil and Maria asked me a few questions, and they suggested once or twice that John asked me questions to explore what my real feelings were.

Neil and Maria had briefed us that part of the purpose of what we were doing was about making sure both of us listened to each other deeply. It was about ensuring we actually understood the other person's feelings, and that it was not about problem solving – which was something John did, as he was very quick to leap in and try and sort out a problem. That really annoyed me, because when he did that I knew he wasn't listening to me, he was just wanting to move on having sorted the problem out.

When they got John to start asking me questions about my feelings, that was very strange, because he had never asked me before how I felt. He would ask me questions like 'How are things?' or 'Have you had a busy day? or 'How are the children?' but never anything other than that. The feelings he started to dig out of me were of being inadequate because of the NCT, dismissal of the fact I had had a caesarean, dismissal of the fact I wasn't breastfeeding Jennifer, and the feeling of being inadequate because I didn't have a lean, toned body anymore, and because I felt a bit fat and unfit and frumpy. I felt inadequate because I wasn't able to do the things that John seemed to want me to do. I wasn't the Stepford Wife. The house he came home to was messy, the food was not Michelin-star standard, and how that feeling of being inadequate actually made me frustrated and hurt and angry, and irritated by him. There was also the feeling of being isolated, that the children didn't need me as much, and I wasn't close to my mother or father and, actually, I felt lonely. To have those feelings brought into the room, and having John actually listening to me as I was talking about this stuff, was really cathartic.

As John was listening I could see he was surprised; and I could see him, in a way, wanting to solve it, but he couldn't. When I heard him say at the end of my part, 'It makes sense to me that you feel sad about my part in our home life, that I am often not there because I am working, and when I am at home I am not really present in the room, I am thinking about other stuff. You are right, I am often not there, and when I am there I am often angry about what I am not getting' I felt pretty emotional.

I was hugely shocked when John talked about his life, about his purpose of earning money so we could have a big house and nice things, and his realisation that all that effort seemed to be going nowhere; in fact, things seemed to be getting worse, as it was just making him feel lonely. Lonely at work, lonely at home, lonely with the children, lonely with his wife. And when he started crying, I wanted to make it all better. I reached over and gave him a hug and in that moment I felt a shift starting to happen. My six-foot-one-inch rugby-playing, strong husband was being vulnerable and crying in front of strangers.

That moment came and went, but it left a sense of hope, a sense that there was a better future which we could both achieve.

The session drew to an end with some more homework, a questionnaire to do, and a request that we had weekly meetings – or State of the Union meetings – and every day we noted three good things that happened that day and shared them with each other, something called the Daily Blessings. Neil and Maria also reminded us that it might be helpful to keep a journal, to keep track of what was happening and how we were feeling, and that this would be really insightful for both of us.

So we parted, and they reached out to shake our hands. Neil shook John's, but then gave him a hug, which I thought was good for John.

When we got back in the car, John's eyes were still a little bit damp with tears. I leant over and put my arms round him and gave him a kiss on the lips. We drove home in silence, but it was a safe and comfortable silence, and for a long time I held John's left hand, feeling a sense of connection to him that felt so good.

Chapter 33: Rachel Tries Communication

Three weeks seemed like a long time to wait for the next session. We had our homework to do, but life carried on as normal. What had changed was hearing and seeing John actually lift his portcullis, expressing feelings and talking about his past. This opened the door to us talking about important things in the past, in the now, and in the future, and I found the exercises in the second session about listening to each other really powerful.

We tried the nightly sharing of three good things. John was reluctant to start with, but it was interesting hearing about three good things that happened to him during the day. Some were mundane, and some were significant. The first thought that came to my mind was the morning walk I'd had with Woody; smelling the fresh air, seeing the sun rising above the trees and seeing his joy as he bounded off in pursuit of rabbits. The second that popped up was lying in bed next to John, now, with him holding my hand and giving me a sense of connection.

I found it interesting that the simple ritual of expressing these good things, of focusing on them and communicating them, made us think about something outside of us and the stuff in our relationship. It helped me fall asleep in a much calmer way, and also feel much more connected to John.

The first weekend after the session I woke up on the Sunday morning wondering what would happen if I made the first move. What if I reached out to John? What if I sought a physical connection?

I reached out to him, and he turned to me, put his arm around me. And for the first time in a long, long time he held me close and we kissed. At first it was a chaste kiss, and then it became more passionate and we made love. It was rather tentative to begin with, as if we weren't quite sure what response we would get from the other; but then it was wonderful, and afterwards we both lay there holding each other close, enjoying the afterglow.

That gave me hope that we could be connected, and we could be in the moment with each other, and we could enjoy each other physically in the way in which we seemed to have forgotten.

The rest of the two or so weeks went OK. We didn't make love again, but we were both busy doing stuff. We did pretty well at keeping the ritual of talking to each other about good things every night, and that worked really well. Twice, at the end of the week, we tried doing the State of the Union meeting, but lack of time didn't help. We couldn't really do it on a Friday evening, and John was off playing rugby on Saturday, and Sunday for both of us was time where we just wanted to relax. So the first weekend we didn't manage it, and the second weekend we did, but it felt a bit clumsy having to stick to a certain way of doing it and we ended up complaining to each other. I complained to John about the mess he'd left all over the place that week, and the fact he had come back the night before a bit pissed. John complained about the house being untidy, and the children not being particularly interested in talking to him. But as they say, Rome was not built in a day, so I accepted the fact there would be ups and downs. Generally, though, things were quite a lot better, and I was looking forward to the third session.

Chapter 34: John Tries Communication

If I'm honest, the second session had sort of frightened me. It was lovely that Rachel leant over and hugged me; and it was wonderful that she held my hand on the drive back. But I was frightened I'd opened a door into my past I wouldn't be able to close, and I wasn't sure what was beyond that room.

Rachel was very keen that we did the nightly homework, and it was quite good fun. It also made me reflect on the good things that had happened during the day. Sometimes they were really simple things, like having a hug before I left for work in the morning and having a welcoming embrace when I got back, but it brought a smile to my face to remember them. It also made me look more at good things rather than focusing on the bad things, and that was a nice way to end our evening before we went to sleep, smiling, sometimes even laughing and holding hands.

On the first Sunday after the second session we made love – and it feels strange calling it making love rather than having sex, because there was a real sense of connection between the two of us. It felt like we were both there in the moment.

We tried the State of the Union meeting, but that felt really clunky and artificial and we ended up arguing. Rachel complained about me being untidy, and I complained about the mess the house was in generally. It was a shame that happened, but it also made me think about how important this actually was, and how much of a distraction it was from the important stuff in life. We got through the next couple of weeks without too many arguments, or bad feelings, and that felt like progress.

I had been open and vulnerable and talked about stuff in the past, and I felt listened to. This made me feel I could do it again, that I could dig inside myself, go behind the barriers and see what was affecting me, and that Rachel could listen to me and could empathise.

I did my homework, and Rachel did hers, and I found I was actually looking forward to the next session and seeing where it would take us.

Each contact with a human being is so rare, so precious,
one should preserve it.

– Anais Nin

Chapter 35: The Third Session

CONNECTION - John

I had filled in something called Bids for Connection – but once again I only did this the night before the session, much to Rachel's chagrin.

Our drive down felt quite relaxed, which was unusual. We listened to some music. I thought I would choose something fairly innocuous, so put Classic FM on, which was OK, but I got annoyed by the breaks for advertisements. I would have preferred Radio 3, but that would probably have been a bit too heavy going for Rachel. So anyway, we had quiet music in the background and had an easy journey.

Neil and Maria were their usual calm, listening selves. They asked about how the previous three weeks had gone, and asked us to give a score for how things were right now. The initial scores we had given were very different. I had scored our relationship five out of ten, and Rachel had gone for two. Now Rachel was at six and I was seven, which was progress. But it still felt like there was a long way to go.

They asked us about significant events in the last three weeks, and we talked about the homework, the State of the Union meeting, and the Daily Blessings, and how that had actually worked well. Rachel raised the subject of us having made love a couple of weeks before, at which I smiled, in a slightly embarrassed way. But she said how lovely that was, and how different, and how she was feeling more connected to me. She reached out and gave my hand a squeeze. Tears started to well up but I stopped them.

They then started to talk about something called Bids for Connection, and explained all the research that had resulted in this piece of work, by Doctor John Gottman in America. A Bid for Connection was basically somebody showing they wanted to connect with the other person by speech, by asking a question, by a touch, or by a look, and how all the evidence showed how good a relationship was by the number of these bids. They also explained how, if lacking, this was instrumental in a relationship not working. They also talked about how for one negative bid there needed to be at least five positive ones, and that there were three possible responses to a bid: turning towards a person, which was acknowledging the bid; turning away, which was effectively ignoring it; and turning against, which was being critical.

They then demonstrated the impact of Bids for Connection on even small things. What they modelled was, 'Would you like a cup of tea, Maria?' Turning towards would be something like, 'Thank you, that would be great.' Turning away might be, 'Can't you see I am busy?' Turning against might be, 'Don't be stupid, I've got far more important things to do.' I could really sense the negativity and the fall in energy in the room from turning away or turning against, and that made me wonder about what Rachel and I were like in this respect.

After we had discussed Bids for Connection, we went through the scores for the questionnaires we had done. We each had six scores, which we hadn't compared before coming back here, mainly because I had only done mine the previous night. The first three scores were about how I made my bids, and Neil and Maria said my bids were pretty hidden, because I no longer asked directly what

I wanted from Rachel because of my fear of rejection. If my bids weren't heard I tended to pull away or express anger, and because of that the bids I made tended not to result in a growth of trust. The second three scores were about what happened when Rachel made a bid to me, and I was shocked at just how low I scored on that. When Rachel made a bid to me, typically I turned away from it. Rachel's scores weren't that different to mine, which wasn't surprising because we were both quite strong people, and quite disconnected. It seemed we both feared rejection.

This exercise was a bit of an eye-opener, and hearing what they meant in our day-to-day lives helped explain just why we had grown so far apart.

Neil and Maria explained how the similarity in scores was OK, and the fact that we scored very low on the important criteria meant there was significant room for improvement in terms of awareness of each other's bids, and how little things would make a big difference.

Although I felt embarrassed, and guilty, it was great to have a sort of verbal instruction manual about how to improve our connections with each other.

Connection is so much about day-to-day stuff, as well as intimacy, so we explored what rituals we had in the morning and in the evening, and the importance of those rituals in reconnecting and disconnecting and reconnecting with each other.

It was fascinating looking at the things we were doing that were unhelpful. In the morning I left early, and Rachel was in bed, so I would go downstairs feeling disappointed she wasn't there to make me coffee, to help me on my way, and that feeling sort of rankled throughout the day. I felt I wasn't important because she couldn't be bothered to get out of bed. When I got back at night, after a long commute, Rachel would often be in the kitchen cooking, or with the children, or on her laptop on the worktop in the kitchen. Woody would be there to welcome me, but he would just get my trousers all covered in hair. The children were often in their bedrooms, and

Rachel would hardly look up at me, and that told me, again, that I wasn't really that important, and the evening would go downhill from that point onwards. Then, when we went to bed – and, yes, we had started doing the Daily Blessings now, but before that Rachel would be on her iPad doing Facebook and stuff, and I would be on my phone checking if there were any urgent emails.

What Neil and Maria suggested was, firstly, no electronic devices in the bedroom at all; that if we needed to charge our phones we did it downstairs; and if we wanted to read something to read a book. The reasoning behind this was when we were in the bedroom we needed to be connected to each other rather than connected to something outside of the room. Secondly, if it was possible for Rachel to get up to say goodbye to me, to give me a kiss, to give me a hug, that might make a big difference to my day. Thirdly, when I came back in the evening, I should pause at the bottom of the drive, and pause before getting out of the car, and take a deep breath and visualise walking in through the front door feeling happy, leaving my work stuff behind and looking forward to connecting with Rachel. Then, when I opened the front door, I should call out that I was back. Then, for Rachel, if she was able to, we talked about how she could come and find me and give me a hug, if we thought that would work for us, and then give me the space to dump my briefcase and get changed. We could then make sure we had time to talk to each other about our days, and be able to offload and share stuff. That all made perfect sense to me, and I hoped we would both be able to do that. Rachel was nodding as a lot of this was being said.

Then we were asked to do an exercise to try and understand our world a bit better, and Neil brought over a big basket of pebbles and I wondered if he wanted us to throw them at each other! He asked us to take one pebble to represent ourselves, and to place it where we needed it to be, and then to choose other pebbles to represent other important people and things in our life and place those where they needed to be. I was a bit confused, and asked Neil what he meant. He repeated what he had said.

I was still a bit puzzled, but Rachel seemed to get it, so I just went with the flow and picked up a large rock to represent myself and put that on the floor, and then chose others to represent Rachel and the children and work and my parents, Rachel's parents, rugby club friends and the house, and laid all those out.

I was asked to explain mine. I'd chosen a medium-sized stone, which was a bit craggy on the outside, as me, and in the middle was Rachel, who was a bigger, smoother stone. Close to her was James and Rowena. Jennifer was a bit further out. My parents, Pip and Ken, were fairly close. Her parents, Dave and Kathleen, were further out. Work was a huge rock, very close to me, and there was a string of smaller, smooth stones which were my rugby club friends, and a big, rugby ball-shaped one, to represent rugby. As I was explaining what each of these meant, I was struck by the distance between myself and Rachel, and the distance between myself and the kids. That brought home just how things were, which was very illuminating.

Maria asked Rachel if she had any comments on mine, and she looked and said, 'Only one thing is missing, and that's Woody.' I told her Woody was hers, and that's just how it was. She looked a bit disappointed, and shrugged. Neil then asked Rachel to explain her stones, which looked very different. Mine was the biggest, in the middle, and had lots of faults and jagged bits in it. Some distance away was her, and her stone was smoother but still flawed. Away from her were four stones – James, Jennifer, Rowena and Woody. The ones representing her parents were closer. Her mum was closer than her dad, though. My parents were some way away, on the other side. That was it, nothing else. *What about her friends*? I wondered. *And what about the stuff she does and her life*?

We were then asked to use the stones to represent our ideal future, and to move, change, add or take away any stones to show how we'd like the future to look.

This was tough for me, and I wasn't sure what to do. I wondered if I could feel closer to Rachel and the children, and how it would feel if it was a real partnership. I chose different stones to represent myself and Rachel. They were both quite large, but a lot smoother, and I put them close together, not touching, but much closer. The children I put like stars around us, with us in the middle. I even chose a very small stone to represent Woody – and Rachel reached over and touched my arm when I explained I'd included him. The parents I left in the same place; and work needed to feel less important and less dominating, so I chose a different stone, a smoother one, and placed it a bit further away. I moved rugby and my rugby friends out a little bit – they were still important to me, but maybe if I felt closer to the family they would become more important, and would have much more dominance.

Rachel did hers and I took a quick peek. It looked similar.

Then Neil and Maria explored what the differences were, and asked me what I needed to happen to get to the new layout of the stones. What really struck home was the big change about connection, and about me being in the right place for Rachel and the children, but also how I saw myself. When I was asked to look at the stones and explain how I felt now, after discussing both layouts, it felt like it should be how I'd laid them out the second time, and that it felt good to think that might happen.

Then Rachel was asked to explain hers, and she'd also chosen two different, smoother stones for us, and we were touching. She'd also added a stone to represent her career, because she explained she wanted to have a career in the future, because that was important to make her feel valued and fulfilled.

With some plans in place for how to better connect, and with an understanding of how to communicate more effectively, there was only one topic of connection left, and I was worried about talking about it. Neil raised the subject of intimacy, and we got talking about when we had made love and what the difference between that and just having sex meant to me. I explained how I had felt so connected to Rachel, and how important that connection was, and how bad it was for me on a regular basis to feel rejected, and to feel my attempts to make love being rebuffed.

We were helped to explore what intimacy meant for both of us, what frequency we needed, and what it would mean if we didn't have it. And, for the first time in eighteen years, we talked about our sexual needs, and what was really amazing was the assumptions we had both been making that we had never, ever talked about – maybe because we had been too embarrassed to talk about them? But given the importance, why the hell hadn't we? We were both guilty of neglecting that big part of our lives.

Hearing Rachel expressing her needs was surprising, especially about her desire for variety and excitement, and to break out of the once a week, same way, same time, same place pattern, and I thought, *Wow! I've been missing all of this for eighteen years*!

We ended the session and I expressed my gratitude for what we had learnt, and my excitement about things we could do differently. We were given some more homework to do, which included a couple more questionnaires, but also the request that we changed our rituals of leaving and coming together again.

We left arm in arm, looking forward to the next session in a couple of weeks' time.

Chapter 36: The Third Session - Rachel

We had a pretty good three weeks leading up to the next session. I had done my homework. John did his – at the last minute, as ever, but at least he did it. We had a good drive down, holding hands in a warm, friendly sort of way.

Neil and Maria explained about Bids of Connection, and how to make sure that for every turning away or turning against there were at least five turning towards. The two of us had been so negligent in making those bids, and receiving them, so it wasn't surprising that our connection and communication was so off piste. That gave me a very clear understanding of what I needed to do differently. John had the same feelings, I think, and understood what needed to be different.

I talked about our State of the Union meeting and how it hadn't really worked and we reverted to blaming each other for stuff. But we got the message. We just needed to keep trying – a bit like a Snakes and Ladders board game, where you can go up, but then land on a snake and go back down again. They also reminded us that we needed to be gentle with ourselves, and be gentle with each other, because what we were effectively doing was creating a whole new relationship from scratch. This wasn't about fixing the old relationship, because we were now eighteen years on, and had three children. Our careers had changed – mine had gone – and life had changed. All we needed to do was decide on our ideal future relationship and create that from stage one.

This was an interesting perspective and made perfect sense, because no amount of sticking plasters would get us back to where we had been. Maybe back then we weren't being true to ourselves,

THE RELATIONSHIP PARADIGM

anyway, as we both had dreams, and we had both gone down this rabbit hole of having stuff rather than having a relationship.

I talked about the Daily Blessings chat and how that had been really helpful in getting us to go to sleep in a much more positive space. Then Neil and Maria explored our departure rituals in the morning, and reconnection rituals in the evening. I felt guilty that all John got from me as he left was a grunt from under the duvet, and when he got back home he was greeted with a slightly grumpy me, who'd had an unfulfilling day. So I made a promise that I would try and get up to see him off, to start his day in a good way, and also to start my day in a better way rather than being annoyed for having been woken up. Why not wake up and feel good about giving John a better start, and also be in a better place to get the children up and get them off to school?

I also realised that in the evenings I was trying to demonstrate to John that I was a busy, important person. That I had cleaned the house (well, sort of), and made a delicious dinner, (with a bit of help from Waitrose), and that I was busy because I was sitting in front of a computer doing things and, after all, wasn't this what John did all day long, so this was me going into his world for a bit? But I realised how important it was to be there to greet him, and to get both of our evenings off to a good start. I also made an agreement that electronic devices would stay out of the bedroom. It pissed me off John checking his emails last thing at night, and I had sort of countered that by posting on Facebook and pretending to my Facebook friends I was having a wonderful time – and also feeling jealous of them posting about their perfect lives. I decided, yes, I would remove the dopamine hit of Facebook and focus on my life and the people who really mattered to me.

A basket of stones came out, which was very unexpected, and we were both asked to produce representations of our life using the different stones, and I got that quickly. John took a bit more persuasion.

I loved the feel of the stones in my hand, and there was a huge selection to choose from. It made me realise just how small my life was when I laid them out, and that felt sad. I explained this to Neil, Maria and John, and they listened, and I looked at John's stones, which were quite different – but I could sort of understand why.

When we were asked to rearrange the stones, to add or take away to produce a representation of our ideal future, I felt so much better. I added a stone for my career, something that would make me feel valued, and would give me fulfilment. I chose a large, smooth stone, grey with a sort of white vein through it, and put it close to me. I also added some friends, away from the children but still close to me.

John explained his 'future' stones, and he had even added Woody, which I thought was sweet. He put our stones close together, not touching, but a lot closer. His work stone was smaller, smoother, and much further away, and that felt much more balanced.

I felt this was a good model for our futures, because what we wanted seemed to be fairly similar.

Then we segued into other forms of connection with each other, and fortunately, or slightly embarrassingly, Neil brought up the subject of intimacy and making love. It was difficult to talk about this, but I also realised how important it was, for both of us; plus, this was a safe space to talk about stuff John and I have never, ever talked about – and it was frightening how much we had assumed. As John talked about his needs and desires I was shocked at how little I knew about what he really wanted. I was also pleasantly surprised at just how similar our needs were. It was very different to what we had been doing! So we explored how we could tell each other, or show each other what we wanted, how we could indicate when enough was enough, or please carry on, and with those tools of openness be able to reignite this neglected part of our lives.

That felt hugely uplifting, and freeing. I could see John was embarrassed, and I felt embarrassed too but, wow, how important it was to get all this out, to have a future where we could enjoy making love, and for John not to feel rejected when I wasn't in the mood. We needed to learn to read each other's signals, and for John to know how to make me feel aroused.

We were given more homework to do, and we also made a commitment concerning our rituals of connection, on leaving and returning, and about our intimacy.

We left arm in arm. I felt like skipping down the stairs. A new future was beckoning!

Chapter 37: Rachel Connects

We had two weeks before the next session and I was excited. I felt like a young girl; like I had the freedom to start our relationship all over again, to talk about what I needed to talk about, and to be connected with John – who I felt I was beginning to fall back in love with. It was a different sort of love, though; a much more mature love where we could be close, and have fun; a love in which we could have a great sex life and, most importantly, where we could be there for each other, communicating well, connecting well and working towards a similar future.

We went to bed and, to my surprise, John came to bed early and we made love, tenderly, slowly, and that felt like coming home. I felt like I belonged.

I heard John stirring in the morning and then he got up to have a shower. I put on a silk kimono and went downstairs and put the coffee on. When he came downstairs, I went up to him and kissed him on the lips, and held him close. He looked a bit embarrassed, and a bit surprised. When he had drunk his coffee, I picked up his briefcase and walked him to the door, and, with a smile, said I was looking forward to seeing him that evening. John smiled back, in a shy sort of way, and thanked me. After I had waved him off, I went and had a bath. I had half an hour before the children needed to get up and I soaked in the bubbles, feeling warm all over, feeling in love again, and that I was no longer trapped.

Now was my chance to create a whole new and different and good ritual for the children, too. My mood seemed to have an effect on them. They were happier, more willing to get dressed quickly, and be in the car on time. After I dropped them off at school I wondered how to spend the rest of my day. Firstly, I went to the gym, and got on the treadmill and worked up a sweat. It sounds corny, but my lingerie was tired and old, and a bit beige, so when I had finished at the gym I bought some more. I didn't go the full hog, like buy suspenders, but bought something black and a bit lacier. I then went home and relaxed and read. I even tried some meditation, which worked for fifteen minutes. I used the Headspace app which I had downloaded but never really used, and that was OK. Then I took Woody for a walk up in the woods, and walked for a couple of hours, feeling at one with nature and able to enjoy being in the moment.

On the way home I went to Waitrose, bought some nice food for John and me, and some OK food for the kids, because at their age all they seemed interested in was pizza and chicken nuggets. I picked them all up from school, and they were happy. Even Jenny had a smile on her face. She asked when we got back if she could make a cake, and part of me thought I couldn't cope with the mess, but a part also thought it would be nice for John. I suggested that she made her dad's favourite, a chocolate cake, and she looked a bit surprised, but got to it. The smell coming from the oven was amazing, and when the cake was finished and iced it looked really good. I almost cried when I saw the message she had written on the top: 'Welcome back, Dad'.

I fed the kids early. Jenny put her cake safely in a tin and I asked her if she wanted to give it to her dad when he got back. She said she would. And then the elder two went off to do homework. Rowena was in her usual fairyland, which was good.

John normally came back at the same time every day, and I could predict when the key was going to go in the lock and thought that tonight I would beat him to it. So I put our dinner in the oven on the timer, and opened John's favourite wine, and let it breathe. I then went and got into my slightly cheesy lingerie, and put on a top that I knew John liked, and some trousers – because I didn't want to frighten him – and some smart shoes. Five minutes before John was due back I was there, near the front door, waiting like a first date.

When I heard the car door close I opened the front door and said, 'Hello, darling.' He looked surprised to see me, and stood there with his key in his hand about to put it in the lock, but he said hello.

I asked him how he was feeling, and he said, 'I'm feeling good. It's not been an easy day, but had a great start, and now I'm looking forward to what the evening has to bring.'

To my amazement, James came down the stairs and asked his dad how he was doing. And then Jenny came downstairs and said, 'I have made something for you, Dad,' and she took him into the kitchen, got the tin out and showed him the chocolate cake. John looked shocked, but thanked her and said he would most definitely have some after dinner. She made him promise to save her some!

Then Rowena came downstairs, and went up to her dad and put her arms around his waist and gave him a hug. 'Hello, Dad!' she said. Again, John looked a bit shocked. I couldn't remember the last time Rowena had given him a hug. He knelt on the floor, and hugged her back, and thanked her, and asked her how her day had been, and she started to tell him what she had been doing at school, and the picture she had drawn, and what she was planning to do tomorrow. It was wonderful to see them connected like that, with Rowena talking about things that were insubstantial and unimportant to John, but important to her.

The kids went off happy, and then it was John and me in the kitchen, and he looked at me more closely and said, 'You're looking good.' I told him I was feeling good, and was happy to see him. I suggested he go and get changed as dinner would be about fifteen minutes.

The food was OK, he appreciated the wine, and we talked about stuff, and then he said, 'Time for cake!' He shouted for Jenny to come down. She didn't hear him as she was probably on her iPhone, so he went up to her room and brought her back down. We got the cake onto a plate and she cut it and gave her dad a piece. And then all five of us sat around the table in the kitchen eating a very yummy chocolate cake, with Woody underneath the table looking very hopeful, but only getting one or two stray crumbs.

It wasn't quite Stepford Wives, but it felt good that I had made an effort, and our home seemed a much happier place to be. I was not sure I could repeat that every night, but at least it was a start.

We went to bed and John thanked me for the effort I had made, and said how much he appreciated it, and, do you know, that was the first time I recalled John expressing appreciation for what I had done, and that felt really good. *We held each other, then, and fell asleep in each other's arms.*

The next morning, I did a repeat of saying goodbye to John, but minus the silk kimono, just my old dressing gown. And by the time I got up he had already put the coffee on, but I gave him a kiss and told him I hoped he had a nice day, and he seemed happy with that.

The evening was a bit disappointing. I was there to open the door and welcome him again, and this time I hoped he would bring me something – a dozen red roses, or a bottle of Chanel No.5, or some Manolo Blahnik shoes, all those would have been nice. He did bring me some flowers, but they still had the price on and were from the petrol station around the corner, so I put on the 'Thank you, that's lovely' face, and felt a bit flat. The children were OK. They didn't do the Sound of Music bit on the staircase, but came down in dribs and drabs. There was still a bit of chocolate cake left, which Jenny was very proud to show her dad, and that was good.

We went to bed.

The routine over the next couple of weeks was OK. It was a lot better than it had been, but not quite as magical as it could be. I did my homework and John, as ever, left his because he was busy at work.

We decided to go to the seaside at the weekend and stay overnight at my parents' house in Bournemouth. James was a bit reluctant because it meant he wouldn't be able to see some of his friends. Rowena was excited, and Jenny was moderately pleased, and John made a big thing about the fact he was giving up his rugby club meeting on the Saturday, but it was good he was prepared to do something with the family.

When we arrived the sun was shining, so we went to the beach at Highcliffe first. We all got into our swimming costumes and did the whole British getting into the sea an inch at a time thing, shivering, even though it was a sunny day. Well, they all did. I decided to just go straight in! It reduces the pain! So I ran, with Woody following me, and dived in, and Woody swam after me, paddling furiously. He was rather enthusiastic, and I hadn't realised until then just how much pain can be inflicted by a dog's claws as he swam to keep up with me. I pushed him away, and watched as John and the kids eventually got their shoulders under water and started swimming, gingerly. It was the first time for a long time that I'd seen all four of them doing fun stuff together.

We swam around, and splashed each other. The water was fairly calm, so the surfboard Jenny had brought down wasn't going to get much use. We then went and sat on the sand and had a picnic, and then got some ice creams, which Woody coveted. After that we packed all the sandy stuff in the car and drove to Bournemouth. My parents live in a big house in a small village, surrounded by farmland, and my mother's garden, of course, her obsession.

Dad wanted to shake everyone's hand, which was a strange way of welcoming us, especially a nine-year-old, but Rowena shook his hand and smiled. My mother put down her secateurs and asked if we would like some tea and cake. There was the usual pantomime where nobody seemed to be able to sit down at the table at the same time, because as soon as my mother sat down, my father got up to go and fuss about something irrelevant, and as soon as he came back my mother got up, and so on. I just gritted my teeth and focused on the fact it was a sunny day, we were in a lovely garden, and had some lovely cakes to eat.

That evening we played some board games and had a chat and it was good fun.

The next day we all went down to the beach, but my mother can't swim so stayed out of the water. We had a good time, and drove home feeling relaxed and happy and strangely connected.

The rest of the time the routine of work continued, and a few times I felt a bit disappointed that John wasn't making an effort, and let my disappointment show. At the end of the week we tried doing our State of the Union meeting, and I was able to express my feelings. I told him how good it was being connected, and having the family working together as one unit. I also told John the couple of things he had done which I found disappointing, and he listened and responded well.

We both did our homework, too, at the same time, sitting at the dining room table, and that actually felt like fun, like we were two kids doing their studying together. We didn't look at each other's answers, but we tried to guess.

A few days later, we were ready for our fourth session.

I wasn't sure what this would bring.

Chapter 38: John Tries to Connect

The third session I found interesting and enlightening, but also quite tough. It was difficult to see the differences in Rachel's world from my world; but it was reassuring to see that in the future we wanted very similar things. Doing things with stones seemed a weird way of working this out, but actually we got to an understanding much more quickly than if we had tried talking about it. I even half-thought it would be fun to try doing this with some of my clients! Some of them were trying to buy companies to make them even richer, and I was wondering what that was all about. When was enough, enough?

It was also really good to be able to understand what Rachel needed from our connections, and our love-making, and for me to be able to express what I wanted.

I was blown away by the reaction I got when I got home from work the next day. Rachel opening the door, looking quite stunning and happy, and the kids even looked pleased to see me. It was a very different welcome home, and Jenny had even made me a cake. When I took the lid off and saw 'Welcome back, Dad', I almost cried. That was a very emotional moment and made me realise just how important the kids are to me. Then we had dinner. Rachel's not the world's best cook, but she made a real effort, and bought me some of my favourite wine and we had a very lovely, mellow evening together.

I went to bed feeling happier than I had for a long time.

The next couple of weeks were pretty good. Work was relentless, though, with a couple of new clients with very difficult acquisitions and not much time to do them in, and that put me under a lot of pressure. But I also tried to make sure the family were more important, and didn't come a distant second to work. Rachel made a real effort to get up in the morning to say goodbye to me, and to make me feel welcome when I got home, and I really appreciated that. We were also able to talk about what had been good and what hadn't been so good, without feeling criticised, and that made a big difference.

I had to give up my rugby to go to Bournemouth for the weekend, but I guess I will have to make some sacrifices. I had to tear James and Jenny away from their electronic devices, and Rowena took a whole bunch of her dolls and fairies and little girl stuff, but we had a surprisingly great weekend, all five of us and Woody. I felt like a real dad…like the dad I wished my dad had been.

Kathleen was fussing around as ever, and Rachel's dad was a bit stiff but seemed pleased to see us. On the Sunday we all went down to the beach together, and David seemed to unfreeze a little bit. Kathleen seemed a bit anxious being away from her garden, but they relaxed and were able to talk and just be happy in each other's company.

The following week was stressful at work, and I tried once or twice to bring some signs of appreciation back for Rachel. The second day I brought some flowers. But nobody ever told me not to buy flowers from a petrol station for your wife. Big mistake. They looked pretty good to me, but I don't think they were that well received. The following week I wanted to bring something back for Rachel. I didn't know what perfume she liked, and I wasn't sure about buying jewellery, so I bought some chocolates and that seemed OK, although the kids ate most of them.

There was still a certain amount of uncertainty between us, and a bit of tension at times, but there were no major arguments, and no shouting matches, so things went well. We even sat down together in the dining room – that we hardly ever use – and did our homework together. I felt a sense of togetherness, both doing the same work at the same time and in the same place.

Neil and Maria had said that if we had any questions or any worries to call them anytime, twenty-four hours a day, seven days a week, or email or text. I hadn't felt the need to do that, but Rachel told me she had phoned Maria a couple of times.

With commitment, all the rules change.

– Robert Fripp

Chapter 39: The Fourth Session

COMMITMENT - John

Once again I had taken the whole day off work, and Rachel arranged her time so we could spend the whole day together. We drove down to Lymington early and went for a walk along the sea wall, looking out at the Solent and just enjoying the views. Then we had lunch and headed off for our appointment at three o'clock. Different time, different day, but the same place. I walked up the stairs feeling an old hand at this, and feeling good about what was going to come.

We were made very welcome, and Rachel went first when we were asked about how things had been since the last session. She said she thought we were able to talk to each other better, and understand each other.

She then talked about bids for connection, and how she had tried to find out what I really wanted, or was asking for, and that our bids to each other were being much better received. She marked us eight out of ten, which was great, and really felt like progress.

I offered my perspective, and gave a similar mark. I expressed my appreciation of the steps Rachel had taken to say goodbye in the morning and welcome me back at night. I explained the great weekend we had had, even with the difficulty of being with her parents. We felt like a family again, I said, and that we had taken a big step forward.

Neil and Maria said we should be applauded for our efforts with communication and connection, and should get ten out of ten for keeping up the Daily Blessings chats and State of the Union meetings, which made me feel like we were on track!

They explained that the third part of the relationship paradigm was commitment: to each other, to the future we wanted, to our family, and to making the relationship work. Relationships happen, initially, by accident or almost by magic, they explained; but making a relationship flourish needs real work, because if that commitment is not there the relationship will simply fade away, because the initial magic will be lost, and the real world will intrude and take us away on different paths.

This was an interesting message to receive, because I had never really thought about a relationship needing work. I had assumed that you met, you fell in love, and you just coped with what life threw at you, growing stronger along the way. But I was beginning to realise I had been wrong, and lazy, because what else in life magically stays the same without work?

We went through the homework, which was about our preferred roles in our relationship. There were seven key roles: Chairman, which was about being dominant and in control; Adventurer, which was about discovering new things; Guard, which involved defending and being vigilant; Energy Monitor, which involved regulating the need for energy, rest and relaxation; Sensualist, which was about intimacy and gratification; Jester, which concerned recreation and play; and finally Nest Builder, which was about creating safe space and attachment.

They talked us through all the levels we were comfortable with, and whether we were in alignment or not. That brought out some significant differences.

For me the strongest was Chairman, about being in control. I was very comfortable with the high level of that, but discovered it was very under activated, which made me feel frustrated and impotent. The second area which was under activated was Sensualist, and this was the same for Rachel. Jester was also under activated, making me feel depressed, as was Rachel's also. She was quite strong on Adventurer. I wasn't. I just wanted things to be much as they were. Guard and Energy Monitor neither of us were particularly strong on, and Nest Builder wasn't high for Rachel, and that maybe showed in the home. This process flagged up our misconceptions about each other, and the specific areas we needed to work on.

The next bit of homework was something called Character Strengths, which had been produced through the work of the psychologist Martin Seligman. We had done a questionnaire online on that one, which helped us to better understand our strengths, but we would do some more work with this.

Using one card for each, we had to write down the attributes we felt made for an ideal relationship, and then place those cards in order of importance. After a bit of thought, I wrote down seven things: family, support, appreciation, love, sex, sharing and independence. Rachel wrote hers down, and we were asked to place them where we thought they needed to be. Again, I felt this was a slightly strange thing to do, but laid them out in a line, in no particular order. But then thought a bit more, and rearranged them in a pattern which, to my surprise, had family in the middle and everything else around it. I was asked what family meant for me. I immediately related the night I had come home, a couple of weeks ago, when Rachel was pleased to see me, and Jenny had made me a cake, and James and Rowena came down and said hi. That, for me, was exactly what family was about.

Support meant knowing Rachel was there for me, to help me through my stresses and strains. Appreciation was about knowing what I did was important and mattered. I didn't expect a thank you for everything, but just the occasional, heartfelt, 'We know you're working hard, and appreciate it,' would be good. I struggled to define love. I have never read much poetry, but love for me was just a feeling in my heart. I knew when I had got it, and I knew when it was not there. It was an instinctive feeling about somebody else that could fade, as it had done with Rachel, but it could come back. Sex was something that had been absent from our life for so long, but it could be so wonderful, and that was important to me. Sharing was about working as a team, dealing with stuff, good things and bad things, and knowing who was going to do what. Independence was about having the time and space to do my own stuff, and for that to be OK, and also for Rachel to be able to do her own stuff, because I didn't want us to be joined at the hip, to be co-dependent. I wanted us to have our own lives, but when we did things together for it to be good too.

We were asked to score our attributes based on how we felt right now, and also on how things had been when we started a few weeks ago.

This I found quite tough, but the before and after scores were quite a contrast. Family scored one initially; but now it was seven, and I explained that was because I now felt part of the family rather than somebody who was just funding them. Support was four, and now it was six. I had always felt Rachel would do things for me, if I asked – maybe not with great willingness, but I could still count on her – but I wouldn't often ask her. Appreciation was originally one, almost non-existent, but now it scored a six. (I didn't want to score it too highly, and make everyone think they'd got this sussed!) Love was three. I didn't feel very loved, and any time Rachel said 'Love you' or sent me a heart on a text message it didn't feel particularly authentic. It needed to be demonstrated not just said. Love had now gone up to eight. Sex, or intimacy, was zero; but now I gave it a nine, because it had gone from sex to intimacy. I then marked it down to seven, because I didn't want Rachel resting on her laurels! Sharing was two, because we didn't really know what was going on in each other's lives. Now it was up to seven, with more to go. Independence was interesting, because I used to feel I could do whatever I wanted, so I'd scored that as nine. Now I gave it six, as it was not as important for me and, actually, I wanted to do stuff with Rachel and the kids much more than I used to. Giving up rugby for a day and spending the weekend with the family had been great.

By the end of this session I felt I understood what was going on in me, and in Rachel much more, and what had gone on. I also understood that a really good relationship requires effort and commitment. We were both asked if we would do anything differently in the coming weeks, and I committed to doing more of what I was doing, to have more family time, and to talk to Rachel more about the future she wanted. She'd mentioned her desire for a career. I needed to understand that, and help her achieve it.

Chapter 40: The Fourth Session - Rachel

I was really looking forward to this session. It felt like we had crossed a chasm, taken a leap over a deep, dark, unhappy place and were now standing on the other side, holding hands, and uncertain what the future would bring, but were moving forward together. I'd phoned Maria a couple of times, when something hadn't gone quite right, and it was great to have her reassurance that these things take time, and not to expect everything to work out right straightaway. She also told me mistakes were OK to make, as we could get through those.

John was happy I'd kept the whole day free, and we walked by the sea and had lunch in the same pub. I had a sense of being more relaxed, us sitting together, looking at the river, rather than us sitting opposite each other, looking at each other and wondering what to say.

We even talked about sailing, and my dream of sailing across to the Caribbean, and John listened this time without being dismissive. He even seemed a little more open to the idea of getting on a boat and heading off somewhere. He said if it was a big enough boat he might feel more comfortable, and maybe he could take some lessons and get used to it. I suggested that maybe we could take the kids sailing in the summer, to Greece or Turkey, and he agreed to that, which came as a big surprise to me.

Neil and Maria seemed very pleased with what we had achieved in terms of the rituals we had done, of leaving and coming back together, and that we were still having our Daily Blessings discussions. It was a bit like going up to the teacher's desk and being given a gold star and being told, 'Well done, you are both working really well'!

The exercise with the blank cards, and writing down my attributes of an ideal relationship, was interesting. John looked a bit puzzled, but eventually started writing. Maria asked me to explain once I had laid them out on the floor – in a pattern which didn't really seem to mean anything, but seemed OK.

My first card was about fun, and I explained how having fun in life was important to me, and affects everything else, making it so much more joyous. Second was love. I felt it naturally when Rowena was born, and James. Love with Jennifer took a bit longer to come, but it did eventually. I had felt love with John, but said that it got lost somehow, over the years, and was only just starting to come back. My third was fulfilment. As senior brand manager at Unilever, I had been making the world a slightly cleaner and better-smelling place, and that had been important at the time. I'd felt fulfilled doing that job. But now, as a mother of three children who were growing up, fulfilment wasn't really there. The fourth card was about caring, and having somebody in life who I knew really cared for me and would do anything for me. Number five was communication, which was being able to talk about the small stuff, the silly stuff and the big stuff, and be listened to. I explained this was something I had only recently started to experience. Number six was support, and knowing somebody had my back, somebody who was there twenty-four hours a day if I needed them. My seventh card was intimacy, and the sense of closeness that led to physical touch, and then to deep intimacy. That, for me, was in the small gestures as well as big ones. Number eight was about friendship, as I needed to be friends with my husband. I said I thought you could be best mates as well as lovers. Card number nine was togetherness, and that was about being a team, and holding each other tight on the rollercoaster of life, and being able to turn to the other knowing they were physically and emotionally 'with you'. Number ten was about excitement. I needed excitement in my life, to be trying new and different things, and to have that wonderful feeling of surfing the waves, with your heart beating strongly, when you encounter a new challenge.

John's scores surprised me. It was interesting how we both felt we hadn't really meant it, about love, when we had said it. I said I felt much more loved by him now, and that I loved him much more, too. I expressed my desire for a career when we were talking about fulfilment, and John actually listened to me. For the first time I felt I would one day have the opportunity to do something I enjoyed again, and that was great.

When we talked about caring, I admitted I didn't feel John really cared about me. Yes, he provided money, but that was just a transaction. He was the husband, and he paid, but he wasn't interested in how I felt. (He'd got a way to go with that one, but he'd done pretty well in the last few weeks.) Communication scored only two originally, as we were hopeless. We were pretty good at arguing, and telling each other what they had done wrong, but our communication was pants. Now it was up to eight, and I had the feeling we would get even better.

When it came to support, I knew John was the archetypal male provider, but felt I would probably have to ask a few times before he eventually got the message that I needed help with something. I was confident of his physical and financial support. I just needed his emotional support, too.

I'd originally scored intimacy a zero. On the rare occasions we made love it was wham, bam, with no foreplay. Now that John understands what I need and I understand what he needs, there is a huge improvement, so my new score was seven. (John, I know you can get up to a ten, but thank you for what you have done so far!)

Number eight was friendship. We started off as good friends, who then got married and had children, and that friendship faded because we stopped doing stuff together and I got increasingly resentful of John not being around and not being included. My score went from two to eight.

My ninth card, togetherness, got the same score. We had been pretty close, but now I felt like we were in training to be together, and were still a little bit nervous about the reactions we were going to get. But to be truly together, you need to be able to take risks and just be open and honest. My last score, on excitement, went up to a four. I was bored out of my mind most of the time, and the excitement I got out of life was pretty small. I needed this to improve, because excitement was important to me, so I said I hoped John could help me with that.

John looked a bit surprised at some of what I said, but seemed to be listening and nodding, even though some of it was possibly a bit harsh. But this was about being real. This was about being honest. And I hoped he understood that.

I was pretty exhausted towards the end of the session, but I think we both understood a lot more about commitment and what it meant. We were asked to pick one of the areas we wanted to work on. John, not surprisingly, picked sex. But what he said was that he wanted me to talk to him more about what I needed in that area. I smiled and gave him a wink. The area I said I wanted to work on was excitement, and that I wanted John to help me get more excitement into my life. He agreed and said, with a smile on his face, 'So, do you want planned excitement or unplanned excitement?' and I told him to go wild, and that spontaneous excitement would be magic!

The session came to an end. I felt we had not only crossed that chasm, but were well on our way to the sun in the distance. Most importantly, I felt we were doing it together.

Chapter 41: This is Really Working - Rachel

It felt like this was, at last, working. I have found the sessions fascinating, and seeing the similarities between us in terms of what we are looking for compared to how we were was actually quite heartening. I could also see that John was beginning to get it, and actually showing commitment to be different, and that felt really positive.

I started thinking about fulfilment, and my career, but I knew there was a lot to consider before anything could progress.

We got back home and the kids were pleased to see us. It felt a bit risky leaving a thirteen-year-old in charge of two girls, but James had promised he would look after them. It was too much hassle to get my parents involved, and I didn't like pretending we were going out with friends – and, anyway, that excuse was starting to wear thin.

I had given them all a good briefing of what to do and who to contact if there was a problem. It had been quite funny listening to the three of them, sat down at the kitchen table, having a grown-up conversation about what they would actually need to make pizzas. (I had also told the neighbours, who we were quite good friends with, to keep an eye open and watch out for any flames leaping out of any windows!)

I wasn't quite sure what to expect when we walked in, but they had successfully made pizzas – and some for us as well. They had eaten theirs, as they couldn't wait, but ours were ready to go in the Aga. They looked quite good! The floor and the worktops could definitely have been cleaned a bit more, but that was no bother really.

John was surprisingly relaxed, and chatted with the kids – something he never used to do much of – and I felt like the five of us were pretty close.

We still hadn't told the children where we were going or what we were doing, and I had given them a half-baked reason for being out all day. I thought it was about time we told the truth, and I explained to all three of them that we had been seeing some people who were helping us to have an even better relationship. Rowena looked a bit puzzled, and Jennifer looked upset and said, 'Does that mean you are splitting up?' I sort of laughed and said we had been together for a long time. With work and children and lots of other things to do, it was quite common for couples to drift apart, and that it can be a really good idea to get some expert advice on doing things a little bit differently, to make life better for each of us, and for the children.

'Yeah,' James said. 'Things are a bit better. You both smile more and are less grumpy.'

Jennifer agreed, and said it used to be really miserable being here, but now it felt quite good.

Rowena rushed up and gave me a hug. And she went up to her dad and gave him a hug too, and she said, 'What can we do to help?'

'Nothing,' I said. 'You've all been great so far, so thank you. But we will let you know if we need you to do anything.' John nodded and smiled, and told them he was grateful, too.

The pizzas were ready, and they were pretty good, and I said to the children it would be great if they wanted to cook some more meals for us!

It was strange how exhausting it had been talking about ourselves, and what we wanted, and when we went to bed we just held each other close. I breathed in the smell of John, and it reminded me of what it was like when I first fell in love with him. I was beginning to feel safe and comfortable again, which was a lovely feeling and filled my body like a red warmth running all the way through it.

Life in the next four weeks ran pretty smoothly. John was making an effort to switch off from work when he came home, and the rituals of leaving and connection were going really well. Talking about the three good things at night kept us very much in the positive.

The love-making became more frequent, too, probably twice a week, and it seemed much more in the moment, more impulsive, and John started trying different things, which was great. I didn't want to scare him off, and he probably didn't want to scare me off either, so we did find it hard to talk face-to-face about what each of us wanted. I suggested to John that maybe we could each write a story, a chapter of fantasy about the love-making that each of us would like, and then read it to each other. He looked a bit embarrassed, but agreed to give it a go. I asked him for a commitment as to when we would do it by, and we agreed the following weekend, so we could read it to each other on Saturday night.

We did our homework. The first was a poem called 'I am', explaining how we had got to where we are now, and what made us who we were. I thought this was quite a scary thing to do, because I had never been any good at poetry, and John told me he really wasn't looking forward to it, either. We both put that off. The second bit of homework was a quiz called 'What do you know about each other?', and it was fascinating comparing our answers and seeing how little we actually knew about each other! Out of fifty questions, we only got about half right, and I felt a bit embarrassed about that! We did find it funny, though, learning all these things about each other.

It felt like we had a few black runs yet to do, which would be quite difficult and painful to navigate, but we were now on the red runs – still quite steep and difficult, but we were going faster, and the valley and the bars and the restaurants were almost within reach and beckoning us on.

Chapter 42: Am I Getting This? - John

The session on commitment was a really tough one. We seemed poised on the brink of breaking through, and I was concerned our cards were going to be so different they would present the reality that we were different people, on a different page, heading in different directions. What really made me feel good was, yes, there were big differences between Rachel and myself, but there was also a significant overlap. I also really liked the fact there was calibration, and that scoring each of our attributes out of ten, as we had been and as we felt we were now, showed huge progress had been made. It also showed us specifically where we needed to keep working, and it was down to us to agree what the priorities were. This felt like real grown-up stuff, to be given guidance but also freedom. By the end of the session I felt in a good place, and Rachel seemed to be in a good place, too.

It was a bit like we were on the rugby pitch. It had been a really tough game, and I felt battered and bruised and wanted to give up and head for the showers, but something spurred me on and I fought through the pain and we got to half time. We were down against the other team, who were a lot better than us, but I thought, *I want to keep going, I want to win this game, it's important.* I could see the kids in the stands watching, and I felt the burden of showing them their dad was good. In the break I sucked the obligatory oranges, and felt my energy start to come back. I saw Rachel in the stands, too, next to the kids, and she was looking at me, waving, and it felt like all four of them were behind me. So, reenergised, when the whistle went for the second half and the ball came to me, I ran, and against all the odds (of what felt like strong opposition) I scored a try. I heard the crowd cheer, and Rachel and the kids started leaping up and down in excitement, and a warm glow of pride filled me. I still had the rest of the half to go, and it wasn't going to be easy, but it felt like I was part of a team and the team was cheering me on.

The next three weeks went well. Work was still difficult, though, with lots of pressures, and a deal fell apart at the last moment, despite all my best efforts. The bank had pulled out after the due diligence report showed there were some problems. But I had two other deals coming good; not quite there yet, but they were looking hopeful. I was working long hours, but it felt like I was making progress. I also sensed my colleagues were more in tune with me; I felt less of an outsider; I felt more part of the team. I even received a couple of positive comments from my boss, which I knew didn't come easy to him.

There was an amazing improvement at home. It was still not perfect, but maybe that was just me being unrealistic. Rachel made the effort most mornings to get up and see me off, and she had started putting little notes in my briefcase, notes of encouragement and love, and it was a wonderful feeling finding them. Coming home at night, I didn't get the brass band, or Rachel naked apart from black suspenders, but I got smiles, and some time with her, and it felt quite relaxed. What was really good was the fact that we disagreed a few times, but mostly were able to talk about it without arguing, and, as had happened occasionally in the past, throwing things around. When I looked upset when I came in from work, Rachel would ask me how I was feeling, and I talked to her. In the past, if she had noticed, I would just have said 'I'm OK'.

In terms of Rachel's goals, I knew she wanted to work on fulfilment, but I couldn't really see how that could change at the moment, with three kids at school. Maybe when James and Jenny had gone off to boarding school? That was an issue we needed to talk about.

Life outside of work? Well, I still went to the rugby club on

Saturdays, and it was fun getting some exercise; but the after-play stuff, the drinking etc, I didn't feel any great desire to do that anymore. Instead I would have a quick pint, but didn't stay and get pissed. I wanted to get home to my family rather than think of reasons to avoid being with them.

And speaking of the family, we've started doing stuff together, like walks. We even went ten pin bowling, which I have never really liked. It's a noisy, expensive thing to do, which is over too quickly, but the kids like it. We also went to the cinema, to see Mamma Mia! Here We Go Again, which I really didn't want to see. Rachel and the kids enjoyed it, though, so that was OK.

How much effort have I been making? Probably not enough. I'd learnt that buying flowers from the petrol station didn't get me any Brownie points. But it was a struggle during the week to find a florist, and the last thing I wanted to do was to get a bouquet of flowers and get on the train with them, and get strange looks from all the other men – who probably thought they were either guilt flowers for having an affair, or else were for my mistress! I bought chocolates once or twice, and sent Rachel occasional text messages asking how she was, which got good results.

I started to think of things that Rachel might enjoy doing. I love to go to the opera, but Rachel really doesn't like opera. Maybe I should take her to listen to some music she liked? I did a bit of research and found out that on the Friday of our next session there was a group on at a local venue – well, not really a group, but a singer and her backing band, a lady called Toyah – who I knew Rachel really liked. So I bought some tickets to keep as a surprise.

The next session was coming up soon, so I did my homework: writing some poetry. Mine didn't turn out to be poetry, really; it was just prose, which was what I guessed you'd call it. I found it interesting, but quite a challenge. I had to switch off the inner voice telling me I was rubbish at doing this stuff, and let the words flow. When they did it felt quite cathartic.

Doing the quiz with Rachel, I felt really embarrassed that I knew so little about the things she liked, and I was disappointed she didn't know much about me either! But it was fun to find out some really important information. It was like a due diligence report on my wife! Why hadn't we done this years ago? The next session beckoned, and could be interesting.

Most of the time I don't have much fun.
The rest of the time I don't have any fun at all.

– Woody Allen

Chapter 43: The Fifth Session

FUN - John

We had a walk before the session and it was great to be in the fresh air. The weather wasn't so good, but we walked along the shore and, halfway along, Rachel stopped and gave me a big hug, which was a surprise. But it was lovely to receive an impulsive demonstration of affection, and it felt better than eighteen or nineteen years ago, when we first started, because there was so much more history between us.

We went up to see Neil and Maria, and it felt like a really good place to be: a place of trust and openness, of safety, where we could spend time free of the rest of the world exploring what was important to us. It was a place where we could shed the past and embrace the future, where magic seemed to happen, because I was beginning to understand the importance and power of a great relationship, not just with Rachel, but with other people, noticeably our kids.

The whole atmosphere at home was so much better. All that time I had spent working hard to earn money to buy stuff, did it matter? Did it matter whether James had the latest iPhone, if we had a twenty-seven-inch plasma TV or a fifty-two inch one, if the car was one year old or five years old? Did it matter what the neighbours thought of our house? What was much more important was the pleasure we got from the kids, and vice versa.

It felt like there had been a substantial shift. When we were asked our scores out of ten, I couldn't give it a ten, because I didn't want to risk us not trying if we started scoring tens, but it certainly felt like nine.

Then came the moment when the actor stands on stage and reads out some beautiful poetry. Well, I wasn't really an actor, and I'd hardly call what I'd written poetry, but the audience was there, and the words were there.

I stood up, and looked at Rachel, and read words which seemed to flow from my heart.

'I am John, born of Ken and Pip.

My father, a strong man but very distant; and my mother, a doormat for my father.

I am John, the only child, but sent away to school at an early age.

I am John, going to boarding school at the age of thirteen, and bullied and laughed at, but learning to fight back and playing rugby, seeking affirmation from my father, but not good enough, only the second fifteen.

Another disappointment beckons as I fail to get into Cambridge, my father's university.

I am John, my mother in the background caring for me, but not able to show it.

I am John, burying my emotions and, on the surface, smiling.

I am John, free at university, doing law because that is what my father wants and playing rugby and drinking and having girlfriends.

I am John, meeting Rachel at a party. Something in her eyes makes me connect.

I am John, I am in love, we live together, and we have a child on the way, and are now married in a hurried ceremony.

I am John, climbing the ladder to become a partner to show my father how good I am.

I am John, commuting into the centre of London, working hard.

I am John, buying a bigger house for my family, now with three children, who I see sometimes.

I am John, married to Rachel, who is fading away from me.

I am John, feeling sad, but real boys don't cry.

I am John, not able to show my emotions, not even sure what my emotions are.

I am John, married to Rachel, who seems to be finding life difficult. She is getting more distant from me, and I just work harder to make more money to try and make everyone happy.

I am John, feeling neglected, unloved, unwanted and impotent.

I am John, working hard to get what I thought I wanted but unhappy.

I am John, getting resentful and miserable.

I am John, given an ultimatum by Rachel: I change, we change, or it's over.

Shit, where has my dream gone?

I am John, on a last-ditch, last-minute, last-hope holiday.

The connection with Rachel splutters like an engine which is misfiring.

I am John, reluctantly opening myself out to strangers.

I am John, rediscovering my wife, my family, discovering love and hope.

I am John, a good man getting to be a better husband, father and friend.

I am John looking to a much better future.'

Rachel was watching me intently, and I felt proud to be able to express my words. She seemed to be quite moved, and she told me how much she appreciated what I had written and thanked me.

Rachel's poem was lovely, and I too felt quite emotional. Neil and Maria also looked moved by her words.

The rest of the session focused on fun, which was a strange thing to talk about. But they explained that fun was fundamental to the paradigm, and hugely important in keeping a relationship growing and glowing. When I reflected on when we had last had fun, it made me realise just what a miserable existence I'd had for so many years. When had I last really laughed, really let go, really enjoyed being in the moment? We had been to a lovely place in Grenada, and there were one or two fleeting moments playing volleyball, and when Rachel and I made love; but for many years there hadn't really been much fun at all. In the last few weeks, though, really simple things with the kids – like eating with them, talking to them, going for walks – had been good, maybe even fun...

Our next homework was called the Bucket List: things each of us would like to do before we died, which made me think that I'd better get on with it, because half my life had probably gone! I left that session feeling good. We were now ahead in the rugby game, and the crowd were definitely on my side. Maybe I could even score another try, and then retire from the game!

Chapter 44: The Fifth Session - Rachel

We seemed to have settled into a pattern with our sessions. John would take the day off work so we could have a relaxing morning and enjoy lunch before seeing Neil and Maria. John told me he had got a surprise for me this time, so we booked a babysitter – the girl who lived next door, who I thought James fancied a bit, because when I said she was going to come and babysit he didn't give me the 'I am far too old to need a babysitter' but instead said, 'Oh, Sian's coming, she's nice.' We told Sian we wouldn't be back until around midnight and off we went.

It was interesting that although the conversation in the car was about everyday stuff it had a lighter air to it. John even told me a joke. He knows he is rubbish at telling jokes, but it was great that he felt relaxed enough to even try! We went for a walk by the sea, and breathed in the fresh sea air, and some of the time we even walked hand in hand. I felt close to John, and halfway along the sea wall I stopped and put my arms around him, and said, 'Thank you, John. I do love you.'

Neil and Maria welcomed us in their calm way and asked what had happened in the last three weeks, and to tell them about the ups and downs. We were both able to talk about the ups with smiles on our faces; but when it came to the downs, John looked thoughtful, and he said, 'I can't really think of anything, which is quite amazing. Thank you, Rachel, it's been good. It's also been wonderful seeing how the children have been affected by how we are and how much nicer it is being around them.'

Neil and Maria then asked us to go through our homework, and we went through the quiz, on how well we knew each other, and they weren't surprised by our scores, but asked what we got from it. I explained how surprised I was at how little we actually knew about each other, but that it had been so helpful, and why hadn't we done that a long time ago!

The second piece of homework was the 'I Am' poem, and they asked us whether we had shared our poems with each other and we both said no. John, to my surprise, said he would go first. He stood up, coughed a bit nervously, and read his. I was moved by the depth of what he had written, and I could see the emotion in his eyes. As he sat down I reached over and gave him a hug and said, 'Thank you, that was wonderful.'

Then it was my turn. I had spent a long time thinking about this, and found it quite difficult. So, one night, I got out of bed while John was asleep, went downstairs and wrote it straight from my heart, and the words just seemed to flow. I hadn't re-read it or checked it, just printed a copy to bring with me today. I stood up and read it to John.

'I am Rachel, wanting to be loved, but not loved or feeling loved.

Idyllic upbringing, but unloved.

I am Rachel, older brother Victor, who doesn't want anything to do with me; Sister Paula, who is OK.

Mother, Kathleen, who loves her garden, but not me.

I am Rachel, my father David, a long way away emotionally, and doesn't show love.

I am Rachel, bright at school, Brownies and Guides, sailing in Christchurch harbour, enjoyable summers with the wind and the sun, but still trying to please my father hopelessly.

I am Rachel, going to a grammar school for girls, goody, goody girls.

I am Rachel, working hard to escape.

I am Rachel, a few stolen kisses, but that is all before off I go to university to study business.

I am Rachel, my father wants me to be an accountant too.

I am Rachel, not wanting to be an accountant.

I am Rachel, having great fun at university, sailing around the country and getting pissed.

I am Rachel, banging my head at rock concerts, in love with Paul, then Martin, but not much love from them.

I am Rachel, in my second year, who meets John at the rugby club party, full of beer and damp French bread.

I am Rachel, I am in love with John, we move in together and it's good, or is it just OK?

I am Rachel, my career away from accountancy beckons, escape from my father's desires.

I am Rachel, exciting job with Unilever, brand manager trainee in soaps.

I am Rachel, making the world a cleaner place, what fun.

I am Rachel, living in London with John, working hard, climbing up the ladder, getting promoted, senior brand manager on soaps, an even cleaner world.

I am Rachel, shocked to discover my mother says that my father had an affair for ten years.

I am Rachel, feeling sad and even more distant from my father.

I am Rachel, getting pregnant, a big surprise. John wants the baby. I am not sure.

I am Rachel, getting married at the register office, only a few friends, no family, a quick honeymoon in Paris and then James is born. My career paused.

I am Rachel. John is an enthusiastic but useless father.

I am Rachel, missing the buzz of work, looking for a bigger house to buy.

I am Rachel, creating a home for James and John, when he is there.

I am Rachel, pregnant again, a big shock. Jennifer ripped from my womb, a difficult baby, difficult birth. I feel a failure.

I am Rachel, evicted from the NCT, no friends, no job. I rarely see John because he is working so hard.

I am Rachel, off to New York for a short break. I get pregnant.

I am Rachel, not wanting the baby. I can't cope with two let alone three.

I am Rachel, having the baby because John wants it.

I am Rachel. Rowena, number three. She is lovely.

I am Rachel, my career is over, three children to look after, feeling depressed.

I am Rachel, seeing my doctor for help, no pills thank you, they go straight in the bin. Speaking to the Samaritans, not much help.

I am Rachel, driving to see my mother, seeking help, being told to just get on with it. John is a good man.

I am Rachel, trying to find my own solutions, joining the local gym, trying to get fit and lose weight.

I am Rachel, hoping the PT instructor fancies me.

I am Rachel, in the club of women bitching about their husbands, drinking coffee in the mornings at the gym.

I am Rachel, Jennifer at school, John gets promoted, buying a bigger house. John's parents help. A huge step, a huge amount of money, a huge load. Trying to find friends.

I am Rachel, looking for something that I haven't got.

I am Rachel, John wanting to send my children away to school. Do I have a choice?

Not much.

I am Rachel, on a slow, downward, unhappy slope. It can't go on like this.

I am Rachel, the last throw of the dice, off to the Caribbean with John.

I am Rachel, finding some help, finding some hope out there.

I am Rachel, eighteen years later, in love with John again.

I am Rachel, this is a difficult journey, but I am so glad I found this one.

I am Rachel, hopeful for the future with John alongside me.'

John's eyes never left me as I was reading; they seemed to be fastened on every word. And although I started off feeling a bit embarrassed, it was lovely to have his full attention and be able to express myself and be appreciated. I sat down, and he said, 'Wow, that was so powerful, thank you, my darling.'

That was the first time I could remember him calling me 'my darling'. It was a wonderful thing to hear, and I reached out to him and held his hand firmly and thanked him.

I could see tears in Neil and Maria's eyes, and Neil said, 'Thank you, that was amazing. Your thoughts were so eloquently expressed, and really powerful. We can see a real connection forming between the two of you, and that is absolutely wonderful for us to see. So, thank you for being vulnerable. Thank you for taking the risk in doing that. Well done, both of you.'

After we had read our poems, we got on to the fourth part of the relationship paradigm, which was about fun. So often people focus on earning money to buy stuff, and bringing up their children, and they lose sight of what fun is and why it is fundamental to a relationship. Neil and Maria said that when they ask couples about fun, and when they last had any, many of them struggle to remember.

I explained that there had been a big change in our relationship over the last few weeks; but when I looked back to the holiday in Grenada, we weren't really in tune with each other at all, and there had been no fun – at least not together. I told Neil and Maria about getting home last time, and eating the pizzas the kids had made, and just talking to them openly and honestly, and the walks with Woody in the woods. It all felt lighter, I said, but in terms of doing silly, childish, fun-like things, and really letting the barriers down and laughing wildly, we hadn't done that for a long time, and wasn't sure if we could.

We discussed what fun meant for both of us. It wasn't on John's list, but it featured strongly on mine, so we explored things that we could do together, and also what we could do as individuals. I talked about my group of friends at the gym, and how a lot of their conversations were focused on their relationship problems and it all seemed a bit negative and a bit bitchy, which wasn't fun at all.

Neil and Maria talked about our bucket lists, and what the top thirty or so things were we would like to do before we died. We agreed we would produce those in the next session.

The session ended positively, with us both learning some new things; but it seemed to be fine tuning now rather than rescuing, and coming from a place where our relationship was actually good and we were trying to make it brilliant. That is certainly what I wanted. I wanted to have a relationship I could be proud of. I wanted to have a relationship I could show to James, Jennifer and Rowena and say, 'This is how to have a great relationship; this is what you need to do when it's your turn.' I also wanted to show my parents that, actually, we were working on our relationship, and we hadn't allowed it to stay in a place where, like them, they just existed together.

Chapter 45: Rachel Has Fun

I left the offices feeling good. John's portcullis had been raised, a lot, but was still there, a bit. We had interesting homework to do, and I felt we had been given permission to tap into the child within, who had been locked up for far too many years and was now being told they could come out and play.

John told me he had a surprise for me: he had booked for us to go to a concert! I thought, *Oh no, I hope it's not opera, I'll die if I have to sit through three hours of Wagner,* but said, 'Where are we going?'

John told me it wasn't far away, and that we could stop and have some dinner on the way because the concert didn't start until about eight o'clock. We drove through the outskirts of Southampton, and stopped at this cosy little Thai restaurant with an intimate atmosphere. I hadn't eaten much Thai food before, and it looked interesting. We ordered, and enjoyed a beer while we waited. And guess what? We sat there like a couple who were sort of in love – yes, in love – and chatted easily and happily until the food came! It was absolutely delicious, and I ate my fair share of the dishes in front of us.

Then I pulled one of the pieces of homework out of my bag, which was called Things to do Together, which had apparently been put together by some of Neil and Maria's previous clients. They'd told us that if we had something we would like to add to it, to tell them. I scanned through the list. I didn't fancy a fish pedicure. They had been fashionable a few years ago, but not anymore. I wondered what we could do right now, which would be fun or different, and I asked John to come up with an idea. He looked through the list, and then he came around the table and sat on the chair next to me, held me in his arms and kissed me – and not just a short kiss you give to friends in public, or even the slightly longer kiss given to a husband or wife, but a real deep, long kiss, the sort of kiss you would only normally have in a private place.

At first I felt a bit embarrassed and tried to push him off, but then I relaxed and stayed in that moment, feeling his tongue gently probing inside my mouth. I responded, and the kiss got deeper and longer, and I was feeling really aroused, so I reached out and stroked John's thigh, and realised he was getting rather aroused, too! After what seemed like ages I gently pushed him away and said, 'Later! But that was lovely.'

John said to me, 'OK, it's your turn now.' I told him I had a few ideas but it would be rather difficult to do them here, so maybe I could do it later on. We paid the bill and drove to the venue. There was a bit of a queue outside, so we stood in the night air, holding hands and moving closer to the front door. When I peeped inside, I saw the posters on the wall, and wow! he had chosen a singer I really loved! I had seen Toyah and her band before, twenty years ago, and she was brilliant, and I wondered how time might have changed her. She played all the songs I remembered, plus a few new ones, and they all looked older and a bit more worn – we all did! – but they were still brilliant, and I really enjoyed singing and dancing along to the tunes. Even John looked like he was actually enjoying himself! In the interval I asked John what he thought and he said, 'They're good. I am almost enjoying it! I'm beginning to see what you liked in them. Before it just seemed like noise and not much talent, but now I can see it differently.' The second half was great, and they did a few encores, and we walked out into the chilly night air. I was really buzzed, and so grateful for the surprise, so I really thanked John for booking it.

The kids were asleep in bed when we got back, so we fell into bed, exhausted.

The next few weeks passed quickly. We both did our homework, and shared ten things we respected about each other, ten things we loved about each other, and some of the things we wanted to do together. We took it in turns to choose, and some of them were really pushing the boat out, and some – like cutting each other's toenails – were surprisingly personal, and the sort of thing you would only expect to do when you're so old you can't reach your own toenails!

Then we each did our bucket list. Mine were mostly about travel! Here are my first five:

Sailing the Atlantic in a small boat
Seeing the northern lights
Travel to the Antarctic
Drive south on Highway 1 in a Mustang convertible
Be a grandmother

I wondered what sort of interesting dreams I would have that night!

Chapter 46: John Tries Fun

I found it really sad to realise that fun had been gone from my vocabulary for so many years, and that the life I had been leading had been focused on earning money to buy stuff to try and make the children and Rachel happy, which was, in retrospect, a futile occupation.

We had the instruction to go out and have fun, and I was unsure what to do. I had booked the concert for Rachel, which I thought she would enjoy, and I wanted to try and share that with her. We were hungry after the session, so I stopped at a Thai restaurant. I'd never been there before, so I hoped it was OK. It had a relaxed atmosphere, and we ate a lot, and it was absolutely delicious. Rachel seemed to enjoy it, too, so I thought this was an evening which was going places. When she pulled her list of things to do together out of her bag, I thought, *Oh dear, what is going to happen now?* I scanned through it, and had a really wild thought: *What if I can do this one thing [on her list] in public?* It had been so many years, so what reaction would I get? The restaurant was fairly quiet, so putting my bravery where it belonged I stood up, went around to the other side of the table and sat next to Rachel, and started to kiss her in a way that I hadn't done for many years – a really deep, passionate, long kiss.

I felt embarrassed to be doing this at first, but I also felt strangely liberated. We had been given permission to do these sorts of things, and it was on her list, so why not? Rachel responded, and my embarrassment dissipated. *That was fun*, I thought, and looked at Rachel. She was still a little bit pink from embarrassment, but I asked her to give me a score out of ten. 'Nine,' she said. *Room for improvement*, I thought, *I'd better get more practice.*

We then drove to the venue. I had never been there before, either. It looked like a converted pub, and there were people queueing up outside. The band I had booked had been big in the eighties, but I had only really heard them at a distance, and hadn't really liked their music, but we got in the queue. Rachel was quite excited. I didn't tell her who we were seeing and, as we got round the corner, close to the entrance, she looked at the list of events and saw who was playing that night and got very excited! I thought, *Wow, I have really scored a great goal here*!

We went in and got some drinks. It was busy, and the crowd were getting more excited as the time to start playing came nearer. With a little bit of a fanfare, a group of five men, grey-haired, one with a ponytail but otherwise bald, came on stage and started playing. They were soon followed by a short blonde lady, flamboyantly dressed, who came up to the microphone, took charge, and started singing. Rachel started bopping around to the music – she was obviously really into it – but I was taking a more measured approach, as it wasn't quite my thing. But soon the energy of the crowd and the music started to get to me, and I thought that maybe I could enjoy this. It made me think how little we had shared about things we truly enjoyed. I had my music, and she had hers. I had my rugby, and she had her gym. She had her books, and I had one or two books. These were things which were really important to us, yet we were never really in gear. Mostly our tastes clashed, or accidentally coincided, but most of the time we were pursuing these things separately. It felt a little bit sad that I had missed so many opportunities to be more aligned with Rachel and enjoy the stuff she was enjoying. It was true of Rachel too, though, as I would have enjoyed her being with me more and understanding me a bit better. Would it have made us more connected, to be sharing these important things?

The concert came to an end, and it was OK, I enjoyed it. Maybe six out of ten. It was useful getting in the habit of calibrating things by scoring them, instead of just saying stuff like, 'Oh, that was quite nice,' but not really committing to an opinion. It was helping me achieve real clarity, and explore my deeper feelings, which was making our experiences together really important, rather than life just being bland and 'quite nice'.

Rachel was clearly still buzzing on the way home, and I held her hand and could almost feel the tingling! It made me think how lovely it was to give Rachel that experience, and to share it with her. It really had been fun.

Work continued to be busy and home was pretty much good. The children and I seemed to be on a different and better level, and I was beginning to understand the inevitable ups and downs of teenager and child emotions. The lovely thing was getting home and looking forward to the reconnection with Rachel and the children.

Rachel encouraged me to do the homework, which we did, and it was interesting sharing ten things we loved about each other and ten things we respected. So many of our conversations in the past had been about things we had done that the other person didn't like, so we had almost forgotten how to praise each other, and to praise ourselves; and it sounds a strange word, but to celebrate the good things.

We worked through the list of things to do together to have fun, and we took it in turns to choose. Rachel said she wanted her toenails cut by me – which, for her, was a brave thing to do because normally she has manicure and pedicure and beauty treatments! – but with a bit of instruction I did an OK job. It was an interesting experience to focus on just one part of my wife's body, to be looking at her feet, holding them, and feeling intimately connected with this end of her body. Then Rachel did mine, which was probably much harder work given that my feet weren't in such a good state, but it felt lovely.

We also baked cakes – and that is something Rachel had never really done; she has always bought cakes, or Jenny has made them. What was really good was that our tutor was a real expert, and to have us both in the kitchen, wearing pinafores as she showed us what to do, was great fun. She watched over us as I made a chocolate cake and Rachel made a Victoria sponge. She was a great teacher, and although both of us got covered in flour and butter and icing sugar it was OK, the mess could be cleared up. Then something Rachel did made it get a bit silly, and we had a fight, throwing bits of cake mix at each other, and Jennifer joined in. I had never done something like that, ever! What would my parents have thought? The three of us were covered in gooey cake mixture, and laughing and laughing, when Rowena walked into the kitchen, having heard us, and looked at us – in what I can only describe as horror, almost – and ran back out again! I invited her to come and join in, but she wasn't keen. We cleaned up the mess as the cakes were baking, and they were actually pretty delicious. Rowena got over her shock of seeing her parents being very silly, which I felt was a really powerful experience for her to have.

Another thing we did before the next session was talk through five things on our bucket lists. I had always wanted to go to the rugby World Cup in Japan, and to learn to play the piano, despite never having learned to read music. I had always envied people who could sit down at a grand piano and play beautiful music. I wasn't sure I had the stamina or patience to devote to hours and hours of practice, but it was a dream nonetheless, and maybe I could start and find out what it was really like. I also wanted to take Rachel to Verona to see the opera in a beautiful setting, to listen to the power of the music, and I hoped this was something we could share. Fourth on my list was travelling from San Francisco to LA on a Harley. I hadn't ridden a motorbike for about twenty years, but the thought of the Californian sunshine, heading south, sea on the right, mountains on the left, and the throb of the engine, with Rachel riding pillion behind me, was so great. Then, lastly, being at the children's weddings. This was many years away, but to be there to hand my children over to the next stage of their lives, as grown-ups in love...that would be amazing. And maybe there would even be grandchildren along the way? Rachel and I talked about how achievable all those things were. Some of them were easy. Some more difficult. But it felt really lovely to have dreams – not just dreams, actually, but plans on how to achieve them.

Rachel's bucket list was different. The first one was sailing the Atlantic, which I guessed, and which I found scary. I didn't really get sailing, and I was worried about the risks and the time involved, but this was something she was resolute about, and really important for her to do. I thought long and hard about it. I wasn't sure whether to put my foot down and say, No, it's unrealistic and unfair for you to want to do that... But I let that thought drift.

If we don't change, we don't grow.
If we don't grow, we aren't really living.

– Gail Sheehy

Chapter 47: The Final Session

GROWTH - John

It felt a bit like if you had been learning to fly, and had reached the point when you're allowed to fly solo; you can take off from the airfield, do a few circuits, and come back and land yourself, yet aware you still have to carry on learning, always – which is how pilots describe flying. Time seems to have flown past since we went to Grenada. In some ways, a lot has happened; but in other ways not much, as we still have so much to learn.

I am looking forward to the last session. Rachel hasn't said very much. She seems happier, though, and although there are inevitable ups and downs, the kids seem to be happier and more engaged, too.

I wasn't able to take the time off work, so we drove straight there this time. We talked a little bit in the car, but Rachel looked thoughtful and reflective.

We started the session with Neil and Maria asking us how we were feeling, and to calibrate our feelings. I gave a score of eight, and Rachel gave a score of nine, which was lovely to hear. I wondered what would get me from eight to ten, and was asked that. My answer was that I felt uncertain as to whether this could be maintained, as it felt a bit dreamlike, and whether Rachel and I could cope with whatever life was going to throw at us.

Neil and Maria told us that this session would focus on growth, because without growth a relationship, like a plant, will quickly wither and die away. Growth was needed to allow both people in a relationship to flourish, and for a couple, and as individuals, to cope with the changes of life, of getting older, changes in career, children and outside circumstances. A relationship cannot remain static, as it was when a couple first fall in love, and it looks very different ten, twenty or thirty years later as people grow older and mature, and change their views and desires.

We were both asked how we felt our relationship had grown, and I acknowledged it had been stuck for a long time. I had assumed that it was OK; that it would just magically stay pretty good, as it had been when Rachel and I first met at Warwick. Looking back, it was quite clear this was unrealistic and it had been foolish to think that. I had lost sight of what was important for me, and Rachel had lost sight of what was important to her.

Neil and Maria did an exercise with us, to help us work out what our values were or things we really wanted in our lives. They gave us a set of cards and asked us to separate the cards into three piles. One pile was the things that were definitely important to us; the third pile was things which definitely weren't for us; and the middle pile was things which we weren't sure of. Having done that, we were then asked to take the middle pile and choose whether they went on the first pile, which was us, or the third pile, which wasn't. I struggled with this, because it involved making lots of decisions quickly.

The next stage was to take a pile of cards that was us and choose seven. I had about thirty to choose from, and this was really hard work. The cards I chose were intimacy, being proud, successful, sharing, contented, loved and fulfilled, and I was quite surprised by my choices, as they certainly wouldn't have been what I would have chosen eighteen or so years ago. I was a bit worried while Rachel was doing her cards and, again, whether they would flag up a real divide. They weren't. Four were quite different, but three were the same. Rachel chose excited, passionate, stimulated and free, but like me she also chose being proud, loved and fulfilled. When I thought about it I realised that, yes, that did reflect the Rachel I knew, the Rachel who wanted more excitement in her life, and who had given up her career to look after our three children.

We were then asked to prioritise the cards, listing them from one to seven. I did mine first, and my order of priorities were number one, loved, as that for me was about having the people I cared for loving me, but also loving myself and loving those people.

Number two was about feeling fulfilled, feeling that the person I was and the work I was doing had a real purpose and made me feel good. It wasn't about the money; it was about making a difference to the world. This came as quite a shock to me, because this wasn't the path I had been following? The path I had been following was all about how much money I could make from my firm. As I thought about that I realised the work I did, did potentially make a difference to other people's lives, as I was helping them achieve their dreams by helping them buy or sell businesses.

Number three for me was about intimacy, which had started to come back. Intimacy was more than just sex; it was about the looks, the touches, the smiles and feeling really close to Rachel; feeling that we could share secret moments with each other and express ourselves in subtle ways as well as big ways.

Number four was sharing, and I think that realisation had come because of spending more time with the children, and sharing my life with them and Rachel, not just going to work, coming back, putting money into the bank and hoping they got some value from that.

Number five was contentment, and that was a weird one for me, because I thought 'contentment' was where people got to when they were retired, wearing beige cardigans and sitting outside their caravan at some caravan park in Devon, looking at the sunset, drinking milky tea and feeling that life was slowly passing them by, in a pleasant sort of way. I realised that contentment was actually having that glow that things were really good, and being in that moment, and allowing the pleasure of that moment to rest inside. That was a really great place to be.

Number six for me was being proud. I had been driven for many years, wanting people to be proud of me, wanting my parents to be proud, and that this had perhaps been an empty goal because of generational differences. I had never really excelled at school, or university. I didn't have any badges or certificates to point to and say, 'I'm really proud of that.' I realised now that all I wanted was for Rachel and the kids to be proud of their dad for doing good things, and looking after them, and having enjoyable times with them. Most importantly, I wanted to feel proud of myself, that I'd coped well with difficult things, and had been able to enjoy life. I wanted, on my death bed, to think, *Actually, John, overall you did pretty well, and you learnt some good lessons.*

Last of all was success, which was similar in many ways to feeling proud. But feeling successful was more than that; it was feeling I had made a success of things, for me, rather than wanting people to say, 'Wow, didn't John do well.' I realised now that that was an empty thing.

So, those were the seven values I wanted to do better at.

When the session drew to a close, we discussed our future plans, including our bucket lists. We talked about creating a dream board, so we could share our future goals. I had thirty things on my bucket list, and Rachel had fifty! We'd already discussed my top five, and her number one, which was sailing the Atlantic. Her others were seeing the northern lights, travelling to the Antarctic, driving from San Francisco to LA in a Mustang convertible, and being a grandmother.

We discussed how many of the top five were compatible, and what was needed to achieve those. I realised we didn't need to be joined at the hip, and if it was really so important for Rachel to sail the Atlantic, then I was pretty sure I wouldn't be going, but she could go. Seeing the northern lights would be good; and we could toss a coin to see whether we went for the Harley or the Mustang convertible!

It felt so great to be discussing this stuff, and it made me start looking at what I wanted to be, and how I could work on the values that were important to me. There would be a lot of thinking and planning going on, I knew that for sure!

The session was now almost at an end, and we were asked what we wanted in the future, given what Neil and Maria had called our 'incredible progress'. We were asked to calibrate where we were now in our relationship compared to how we had been when we first started, and the difference was huge.

They reminded us that we needed to keep working at 'us', and that they would be there for us at any time in the future if we had a problem or any questions.

I felt glad that we'd had this experience, and felt sad it was coming to an end. But I also felt reassured that the door was still open. Some couples came back on a regular basis, they explained, maybe once a year for a relationship MOT, to make sure everything was still working well and they were on track. We both said that sounded like a great idea.

We all hugged, and off we went, back home, back to our family, my family, and our future together.

Chapter 48: The Sixth Session - Rachel

Our last session was coming up and I felt a bit worried, like I had fallen out of the boat, I was wearing a life jacket and it had inflated, and John was with me, but we now had to take the life jackets off – Neil and Maria – and go it alone.

We had Radio 2 on in the background on the way down, which was playing fairly average music in between pretty inane comments by the DJ.

Neil and Maria told us that in this last session we would focus on growth. For me, doing the values, I was a bit surprised at how fulfilment was so important after having fallen off my career ladder and become a – sometimes – reluctant mother. I also sensed from John's choices that he was seeking more than just being a high-earning lawyer, so I wondered what direction that would take him in. That made me feel excited, but also rather nervous, because we might end up setting off in separate directions, and how would that affect our relationship, which, after so long, was in a good place?

I knew that seeking praise from my father had been a pointless pursuit, and that I wanted to feel proud of myself and for John to feel proud of me. I needed stimulation, too, because a lot of the time I was bored, especially with the girls at the gym, who just seemed to want to drink coffee and Prosecco and complain about their husbands and boyfriends and giggle about their crushes on the hot PT instructors. That didn't feel like me anymore. I wanted to be excited and passionate about doing something that meant a lot to me.

There were differences in our values, but not significant, and that felt good as there was compatibility between them.

I had never thought about my bucket list. I'd had dreams, which would appear and float away again, but to actually write things down on paper felt like committing to them, and that was a bit scary. My list had fifty items on it, whereas John only had thirty. Maybe that was because I had more time on my hands, and a whole heap of frustration about wanting to escape.

Many of my choices were about experiences, about going to places, doing different things – and sailing the Atlantic was top of my list. It would be such an exciting and challenging thing to do; on a small boat, with three thousand miles of ocean, which could be rough. Conditions could get really difficult, but the wonderful feeling of accepting the challenge, of heading off into the unknown and being, for three weeks, out of reach of land and other people – knowing your survival was in your own hands and nobody else's – was so appealing to me. I knew it was very unlikely John would want to do this, but it was very important to me.

I must say I didn't fancy riding on the back of a Harley, but that is what John wanted. I wanted to be in a Mustang, so maybe we could come to some agreement on that. The thought of being a grandmother surprised me, but dovetailed with John wanting to be at the children's weddings.

I now fully understood the need for growth. I had been shrinking for years, in ever nicer homes with less meaningful things to do, with no real purpose. The possibility of having a purpose was in my hands now, in my relationship with John and for myself, and that was so great. It felt like we had both come a long way in a few months. Before we had gone to Grenada, I never imagined we could have a brilliant life, and a brilliant relationship. It was like we were supposed to go out there and meet Olivia and Richard.

When the session came to an end, I felt reassured that this wasn't the end of our relationship with this wonderful couple; it was just another stage in our growth, and they would be there for us if we needed them in the future. We knew we could come back to check we were still on track, and that was comforting.

We all hugged, and John and I were given 'gold stars' – not literally! – for how well we had done, and how far we had come in such a short space of time. I felt proud of what we had both achieved, of not having walked away from John and choosing to make something of our life together. Splitting up would have been tough on the children, and tough on us. And to have stayed as we were – unhappy with each other, and heading in the wrong direction – would have been an awful waste of possibilities.

I thanked John, from my heart, and we headed back home. Even the word 'home' had a resonance now, and felt like a place I wanted to be, with people I wanted to be with. It was a sanctuary for all of us. It was no longer a showcase to impress the neighbours and friends. It was a place for us to feel good in.

I couldn't wait to get home and carry on our good work and see where it took us.

If trust becomes questioned, the clouds of mistrust sweep in and create uncertainty, a lack of clarity and confusion.

– Neil Wilkie

Chapter 49: Rachel Plans Growth

I left our sixth session feeling excited, but also nervous and worried that I had lots to do. I had to keep life going the way it had been, and I also needed to work on what I wanted for myself in the future. On top of all that, I needed to work with John on continuing to keep our relationship developing; to pay attention to our communication, our connection, our commitment to each other and growth, but in the midst of all that stuff to have fun as well.

I decided I would buy a new notebook and start planning this out. I suggested to John that he might like to join me in working out a plan, and he looked a bit surprised but agreed. Knowing that John often puts things off, I suggested we make an appointment to do it, and we agreed that next weekend the two of us would sit down together for a couple of hours and plan out our futures.

Having agreed that, a whole weight seemed to lift off my shoulders and, on the drive back, we talked about all sorts of things, and it almost felt like we were starting a whole new relationship. It was exciting, and I felt a tingle running down my back, and a feeling that, actually, I was in control and wasn't drifting any longer.

We got back home and the kids were doing their stuff, glued to their electronic devices, but actually took a break for a few minutes to say hi. I cooked dinner – well, to be truthful, I got stuff out of the freezer and put it in the Aga – and John and I sat at the kitchen table and talked about what we were going to say to the kids. John was reluctant to say much more to them about what we'd been doing, but I wanted to tell them, in summary, what we were aiming to do. John eventually agreed it would be best to be open and honest with them.

Dinner was ready, and the kids trooped down without being shouted at, and we all sat around the table. Things were relaxed and family-like; quite different to how it had been a few months ago. We had decided that electronic devices would be banned at the table, as they were a huge distraction.

When we started eating, I said, 'James, Jennifer, Rowena, we've got something to tell you.' They looked worried. Jennifer looked down at her food, Rowena looked a bit confused, and James gulped. 'Actually, it's good news,' I added, and they all said 'Phew!' in unison! 'You know we have been having counselling over the last few months, because things had got to a place which wasn't good,' I continued. 'Well, your dad and I made the decision that we needed help, and we've worked hard and are now in a much better place. I think you've picked up on the fact that the two of us are actually much happier now, and that we're more relaxed and appreciate the important things in life?'

I looked around the table and got three grunts. The kids were all beginning to look slightly embarrassed now, but I carried on.

'What we both realised was that we weren't doing the best we could for you. We love you a huge amount. You are really important to us. And we're sorry if our arguments have worried you, and that we haven't been very happy parents at times.' John nodded his head in agreement. 'We've been trying to change that over the last few months, and I hope we are now in a better place with you, too. What we need from all three of you is feedback if you think we are failing in our duties as parents.'

They carried on eating. But I still carried on, hoping they were listening to at least some of this.

'What we also realised was the importance of talking about our feelings, but without arguing, and creating good feelings, and enjoying life, so that is what we are focusing on from now on, and we want your help with that. Can you give us that?' More semi-grunts. 'Is there anything any of you would like to say to us? We would really appreciate that.'

There was a long pause, and then James spoke up and said, 'It feels a bit weird talking about this, but, yeah, it's been a lot better. I'm not used to my parents talking about feelings, but actually it feels good that you are able to do that.'

Jennifer nodded her head. 'Yes, it's good. Weird, but good.'

Rowena jumped off her chair and gave me a hug and said, 'Thank you, Mummy, thank you.'

John said a few words then, backing me up, and I told them, 'We want to plan our futures together so that we're doing the work we want to do, having the fun we want, and keeping our relationship growing too. What would be really helpful, is if the three of you start to think through what you want out of life, right now and in the future, and maybe we could talk about that. And maybe once a week, over dinner, we could have a family conference and talk about what has gone well, and what has gone not so well, and what needs to happen differently in the future.'

The three of them looked really puzzled for a moment, and then said that would be good.

I stopped talking, and things relaxed again, and the food got eaten up. I was delighted when all three kids got up from the table, picked up their dirty plates and actually started loading the dishwasher!

I then told them we had bought a whole range of ice creams for afters, and asked Rowena if she wanted to get them out of the freezer. She opened the freezer door and said, 'Wow, there is loads here! Which ones do you want?' I asked her to bring them all, and said we could go wild, and could she find the hundreds and thousands and chocolate sprinkles to put on the ice cream too. 'And the chocolate sauce and the raspberry sauce?' she asked, and I laughed and said yes. We ate loads, until there was very little left, and I felt very full!

The children were being remarkably mature about all this, and that felt like another weight off my mind, being able to be open and honest and share some of this stuff.

John and I got into our new routine, taking time to connect with each other, and being very careful that the pressures of day-to-day life didn't swamp what was precious. I started to do more work on what I wanted in the future. I had loads of self-help books, all about being the person you want to be – most of them written by people whose photographs made them look very beautiful, very happy and very successful – and I couldn't help but wonder what was really going on in the lives of these seemingly perfect people. I now realised that actually I had the tools and the intelligence to find my own answers; I'd just needed to create an environment which allowed me to open up to possibilities, where it felt safe and comfortable, but also where I could challenge myself.

I also looked again at my bucket list, and I discovered a site called The ARC, the Atlantic Rally for Cruisers which started in November from Las Palmas and finished in St Lucia in January. There was a page on the website for people looking for crews, and people who wanted to crew. I put my name down, just out of interest.

I waited for emails from people who might want me to crew for them, and I investigated what sort of qualifications might be helpful. I had done lots of dinghy sailing, but very little big boat sailing. I found courses – Competent Crew, Day Skipper, and even Yacht Master –and decided Day Skipper sounded good. A week-long course would give me better experience of navigation and big boat handling. I reserved a place on the course, for three weeks' time, and decided I would tell John at the weekend.

The weekend came and John and I went for a walk. I don't think he realised how serious I was about sailing the Atlantic until I told him I had put my name down for possible crewing places. He looked really shocked, and asked when I might go. I told him it might be this year, maybe in a few months' time. He looked really upset, especially when I told him about the course, and he asked how I could do this without talking to him, and how did I expect him to look after the children, and what about him. He then got really angry and started shouting. I wondered whether to hold my ground, or give in? Maybe I was being unreasonable?

I thought long and hard and then said, 'No, John, this is important. It's important that we pursue our own lives, too, so that we can both grow. Let's talk again this afternoon, about what is important for us both.'

He didn't say anything, and the rest of the walk passed in silence, which felt awful. Our discussion that afternoon didn't happen. John said he wasn't in the mood. It was then that I realised: I had damaged the trust we had built up that we would be open and talk about our plans and feelings by not telling John at the time about my course and putting my name down for crewing. I felt really bad.

On Monday morning I got up early to make him some coffee, as part of our ritual of saying goodbye. He barely looked at me, and I said, 'John, we need to talk about this. When can we talk about it?' He said he didn't know, and that he was very busy, and then stormed out of the house. I sent him a text later that day saying I loved him, and that we did need to talk about this. I got no response. I was upset and didn't know what to do.

I didn't have anyone to talk to about this, so I dialled Maria's mobile number and was surprised when I got straight through to her. She listened intently as I explained what the problem was, and how I was feeling. I thought John and I had come to an agreement, I said, but that seemed to change as soon as I'd started to put one of my plans in place. She underlined how important it was for John and I to have a proper conversation and express our feelings about this topic, as they had taught us to do. She emailed me, as a reminder, their structure on how to have a difficult conversation, how to focus on whatever feelings were emerging in both of us, and what outcome we wanted. I found that talk helpful and it calmed me down.

That evening John was two hours late, but I still rushed to the door when I heard his key. He was trying not to look at me, and I went up to him and touched him on the face and said, 'Welcome back,' but he was stiff and tried to shake me off. Feeling dejected I said, 'OK, I've made dinner for us. Let's go and eat in the kitchen, when you are ready.'

Ten minutes later he came down and I had done my best. I had even lit a candle and had a bottle of wine ready and open. I asked him how his day had been and he said, 'Same old. Going round faster and faster in circles. It seems to be endless.'

'That must be tough for you. What can I do to help?' I asked.

He looked at me and said, 'Maybe don't bugger off and leave me to it.'

'When would you like to talk about this?'

He sighed and said, 'Let's get it over and done with.'

'John, I love you. I thought we had got through the worst, that we were on a good path now. We agreed what was important to both of us, separately and as a couple, and things were going really well until I started doing something for myself, like number one on my bucket list. I feel sad that I am being held back from doing that.'

He looked at me and said, 'It just doesn't seem fair that your dreams are the priority now, not mine.'

'OK, well let's talk about your dreams. You wanted to go and watch the rugby World Cup in Japan. What's stopping you from doing that? You want to learn to play the piano. Again, what's stopping you doing that? And you want to be at your children's weddings, and I want to be there, too, and be a grandmother. So some of what we want is different, and some is the same. What is it that is really upsetting you about me wanting to sail the Atlantic? Tell me how you are feeling about it?'

'I feel angry.'

Remembering what Maria told me, I dug further for the feelings, so I said, 'You feel angry. Anything else?'

'I feel upset.'

'Anything else?'

'Yes, I feel sad, and a bit alone that you are doing your things and I am lost really, not sure what I want to do.'

'I can understand that. What can I do to help you find what you want to do?'

John sighed again and said, 'Maybe talking about it is helpful, but maybe I need some more help. I don't like it when you make big decisions without conferring with me. It makes me feel powerless; it makes me feel you are in control.'

I reflected on that. Maybe it was strange for him that I had started to take control, that I was no longer just staying quiet and spending his money and doing stuff to keep the house going. I wondered if he was frightened of the new Rachel? I said, 'I would like you to be interested in this with me, not sailing the Atlantic, but involved. And then why don't we do something together to help us both grow?'

John thought about it. 'Yes, maybe that would be good. I don't know what, but let's talk about it.' He drank some wine and then said, 'Tell me about this sailing thing. I don't get it.'

So I explained my love of sailing, and the feeling of freedom and challenge, of hurtling through the waves in a small boat.

He said, 'OK, how much will it cost?'

'Not a lot, I don't think. I just pay for my share of food and the flight back. It takes about a month.'

'What about the children?' he asked.

'I will speak to my parents. I'm sure they'll be happy to come and help out.'

'The course?' John said.

'That will teach me important skills I need, and I think it will only be a few hundred pounds.'

He had another swig of his wine. 'How important is this to you?'

I held his hand and said, 'John, this is really important. Not as important as us, but it is significant. I really want to do this.'

'OK, then let's talk about things we are going to do together. I don't want you going off and losing you again.'

'I have found you properly, John,' I said. 'Maybe for the first time. You are not going to lose me, and I do not want to lose you. Hold onto that.'

Later, when we went to bed, John's anger had subsided, and we held each other and I felt close to him again.

The next day I booked my course, paid the money, and had an email from one of the competitors on the Atlantic Rally for Cruisers wanting to meet up to talk. They sounded interesting, and they explained their boat and who they were – a couple and a male friend who wanted a fourth member of crew – and although I was a bit worried about the 'male friend', we arranged to meet up in two weeks' time. They were down on the Hamble, which was where my course would be, so I said I would visit them one evening while I was there.

Chapter 50: John Tries Growth

Things with Rachel were good, so much better than they had been; but it felt too easy, too quick somehow. How could something so significant have been turned around in just a few weeks? I felt worried it would fall apart very quickly, and we would go back to where we were; but I was also excited thinking about my future, about what I really wanted. However, I didn't know where to start.

It felt like Rachel had the bit between her teeth and knew what she wanted, and I was some way behind her. She was racing into the future, and I was standing there, wanting to be with her, but also not sure where that path was leading. I'm not as impetuous as Rachel. I needed to have my future more clearly set out. Carrying on doing what I had been doing seemed the obvious thing to do, as that was what I had spent so many years training for and working for. Rachel had the freedom to do whatever she wanted, and I was the man who was going to pay for that. I just had to carry on working to keep the house, the children and Rachel, and carry on climbing that ladder to wherever it might lead me.

To have three children who were talking and interested seemed unreal, and I didn't know how that had happened; and to have a wife who waved goodbye in the morning, greeted me when I came home, and made me dinner – well, sort of – was great, so why couldn't I relax and enjoy it? Why did it all feel a bit false, a bit Stepford?

Rachel instigated a family conference and, wow, that was weird, talking openly to the children about what we had been through and what we wanted. We had never done anything like that before, and the reaction of the children was amazingly mature – where had that come from? They were part of my DNA, and I felt a sort of glow of pride in these three children, who I had helped bring up.

It made me think about the 'conversations' I'd had with my parents, which were all about focussing on being on the rugby team, getting good grades and getting to Cambridge. There was no talk of how I actually felt about anything. No wonder I couldn't just shake off my heritage and be this new, modern dad who did talk about stuff. And heaven only knew what my father would think if I told him I was contemplating taking off, giving up nearly nineteen years of a career and doing something different. Then there was the reality of the running costs of a big house, the mortgage payments, the expensive school fees – that they were paying; well, at the moment – and keeping Rachel in gym club membership. I had to carry on working; there was no escape. Or was there?

Things were great until the weekend Rachel and I went for a walk. Woody was doing his usual bit, running off after rabbits in the woods, and Rachel told me she had been making inquiries about sailing across the Atlantic in a few months' time, and that she had booked a sailing course. I was shocked, and angry. How on earth could she do this without talking to me, without getting my agreement? What had happened to our promise to talk to each other about our thoughts and plans? It was a dangerous thing to do, and who was going to look after the children, and me? It was all very well for her to chase her fantasies, but what about mine? I felt Rachel had broken my trust, and I felt awful.

Maybe the bubble had burst. I couldn't say anything to her. We walked back in silence. I was half expecting her to say that she'd been joking, but she didn't. When we had dinner that evening she started talking about it again, but I really wasn't in the mood. She made me talk about it, though, and it felt like she was my counsellor, asking me how I felt, which was quite invasive. What business was it of hers how I felt? Then I thought, *What on earth am I thinking? Of course it's her business how I feel. Isn't that what love is about, sharing feelings?*

I started opening up, and she helped me come to the realisation that actually this wasn't about me, and it wasn't about her, it was about my past; it was about not being allowed to do the things I really wanted to do, and it felt unfair she was making one of her dreams a reality. Who would I be, and what sort of husband would I be if I didn't help my wife pursue her dream? But it still felt uncomfortable. But then what if the boot had been on the other foot, and I knew what I really wanted to do? Would Rachel back me on that? Maybe she would.

The next day I felt distant, but when we talked again that feeling faded. I decided it would be helpful to talk to somebody, to get a different perspective on my feelings. I called Neil and left a message, and he rang me back an hour later. I was able to get some privacy at work and we talked for about an hour about what was really happening for me, and why I was upset about Rachel wanting to go off sailing, and that I felt she had broken my trust. I talked about my past, too, and my dreams and my uncertainty about what I wanted, and my feelings about letting Rachel pursue her dreams. By the end of that call I felt much better about letting go and allowing Rachel to do what was important for her. I also felt a sense of being given permission to seek and pursue my own dreams, to leave the past behind and become the John who was authentic and committed to his goals.

That evening I talked to Rachel and told her about the conversation I'd had with Neil, and she raised her eyebrows and looked surprised. Then I said, 'Of course you can go. I know how important it is for you. I just want to know it's going to be safe. So, please, involve me, let me know the details, where you are going and who you are going with, so I can back you and support you.'

She gave me a huge hug and said we should start working on my dreams.

My dreams. Wow. How was I going to make them happen?

Only the wisest and stupidest of men never change.

– Confucius

Chapter 51: John's Future

Finding the steps to pursue my dreams was top of my agenda now. It felt like a sense of competition with Rachel, though; that I needed to be alongside or even ahead of her. Was that wrong or right? I phoned Neil the next day and discussed this, and he suggested I probably needed three sessions to work on getting me to the future I wanted. I booked them, a week or so apart, and that evening I told Rachel what I was doing.

She looked a bit worried and said, 'Is this about you or about us? Because if it's about us I want to be there with you.'

I said, 'No, this is about me. This is about my future, my dreams. You have found yours, easily.'

'I haven't found my dreams. I've just organised one thing on my bucket list. I don't have the answers yet to all the things I'd like to change in myself.'

'So you need four weeks across the Atlantic, and I need three or four weeks in Lymington. Mine is going to be a bit easier to organise than yours, is that OK?' I sort of laughed, wondering if she would get angry.

She smiled. 'Yes, yours will probably be cheaper and drier and a bit easier, and the food will be better.'

'OK, then. Let's see who gets the best solution,' I laughed.

Life at home carried on as normal, and life at work was pretty much the same. It all seemed to be about raising money to do deals to help other people and their dreams, however, and I started to wonder whether the dreams those people had been pursuing were fulfilled when they got that acquisition, when they got that sale. I'd never asked them 'How was it?' My role ended once the deal was done.

I decided an interesting thing to do would be to get in touch with some of these clients from the past, and maybe meet up with them for lunch and ask them where their dreams were now. I went through my list and chose three clients, and emailed them. I got two positive responses, and one didn't reply at all. I phoned up this third one, who was surprised to hear from me, but he agreed to meet for lunch.

What I found was surprising, and concerning. The first one was an engineering business with about a £50m turnover. He had sold his business, after running it for twenty years, to a PLC, and he had been on a two-year earn out, and the performance of the business in that two years would determine what his final payment would be. When I met him he looked tired. I remembered how excited he'd been about the sale, and when I asked him about what had happened in the interim, he said it had been tough.

'Suddenly the company I had spent twenty years building up had been taken over by these people,' he explained, 'and they didn't really care about my staff, or the culture I had built up, they just wanted to get as much money out of it as possible. Yes, I got half the money up front, but the other half would be settled after two years, and although I didn't like it I couldn't walk away, the money was too significant.

'I stayed, but I hated what was happening around me. I hated that people I had known for twenty years were being made redundant. I hated the fact that any time I wanted to do anything I had to get permission from them. I hated the fact that they played tunes on the numbers to reduce the amount I actually got after two years. I felt like it wasn't their business, but it was.

'After two years of hard work I got less than half of what I deserved, and that felt really bad; but what felt even worse was my legacy was no longer there - they had cut it to shreds. Two years after the deal was done, I had no job. I had money in the bank, enough money so I would never have to work again - not as much as I'd hoped for, though -and for the first time I started to think about what I really wanted.'

Mark looked at me, his face serious. 'When I started down this path with you some years ago, I thought all I wanted was a sum of money in the bank and then my problems would be over; I could relax and enjoy doing whatever I wanted to do. But, John, when I got there, OK I could buy a bigger house, mortgage-free, and I could buy another car, but my wife, who had stood beside me while I had built up the business, didn't like having me around twenty-four hours a day, and I felt like an intruder into her life. She had a big group of friends who weren't interested in me, and I certainly wasn't interested in them. The children had gone, and had their own careers and their own families, and we could be occasional grandparents, but the money made no difference to that.

'We had the choice of buying a villa in Spain or France, and going there for months on end, but I realised that my wife and I actually didn't have much in common. It was almost painful to be in the same place as her with nothing to talk about, and I hated golf; in fact, I hadn't had any time to build up any other interests, so I was left feeling empty. I'd devoted twenty years building up to this moment, and now it was pointless. I drank a lot, which didn't help. I slept in with a hangover, and that didn't help either. I didn't have many friends, as most of my friends had been at work, and they were unhappy because of what I had done, and many had lost their jobs. So life was looking pretty bleak.

'A year or so ago I started looking for something I could do, to bring me some sort of satisfaction. What had I been pursuing all this time? I still don't really know. I do know I've been on the wrong path for so long. I am looking to the future, but not really sure what that future is. I have given up the drink, and things with Joan are OK, but I spend most of my time just walking, reading and letting the days go past. It all seems a bit of a waste.'

I said, 'Mark, if you had known this two or more years ago, what would you have done differently?'

He said, 'I think I would have held onto the business, and I would have built a management team, so they could run it, and I would still have some involvement, so I could make sure my legacy would carry on.'

I left that lunch feeling sad for Mark, and sad that the work I had done hadn't really helped him.

The next lunch I had was with a lady called Gemma, who had run a very successful business. She had taken the business over from her father, and built it up with a very strong culture. At a young age she was approached by a PLC, who wanted to buy her business, and her story seemed so similar to Mark's. She had sold, she had been on the earn out, and she was, as she put it, 'trapped, watching her business pulled apart, watching her legacy torn down and her culture stripped'. She too had money in the bank, but once again no clear idea where to direct her considerable abilities and passion.

I asked Gemma the same question I had asked Mark, about doing anything differently, and she said, 'I wouldn't have sold. I would have held on, because actually I enjoyed running my business. But I would have spent more time building other interests, because what I really love is helping other people grow and develop and prosper. I could then have used my skills and time doing that. I have started doing that now, but it's much easier when you have an existing business, as it gives you credibility. People don't put much store on somebody who once had a business that no longer really exists. People also, like myself, get much more value out of time when time is precious. When I wake up every morning and feel that time is endless, and I can choose whatever to do, it feels empty.'

I was beginning to see a pattern here, and my third lunch was coming up – which wasn't doing much for my waistline or my feelings of self-worth.

My third lunch was with Robert, who had been running a very successful retail business. He acquired another one, with a substantial amount of money involved, about £50 million, and I had read some things about this new business in the financial press.

When I met Robert I was surprised at how he looked. He had put on a lot of weight, and looked a lot older. We talked about life in general, and then we got around to business, and I asked him how things had been since the acquisition.

He said, 'Wow, it has been really difficult. I started this off with high hopes. The business seemed a perfect fit, and would take us to a whole new league, but now my problems seem ten times as big.'

He explained how, from the outside, the business looked all shiny and well run, but on the inside was quite different. A third of the staff seemed on side, but the other two-thirds were either indifferent or resentful. They didn't like the fact that things had changed, even though he believed they had changed for the better. He received a shocking amount of 'terrorism', as he called it, and most of his time was spent weeding out the negative people who didn't fit. Profitability was nothing like it was portrayed to be, with a major drain on cash. He'd now got the bank and a private equity house on his back wanting instant results, and no excuses.

I was really sorry to hear all this, and asked him the same question I had asked Mark and Gemma.

Robert replied, 'I sure as hell wouldn't have done that deal. I did it because I thought it was important to grow, to be bigger. But why did I actually need to be bigger? What was that all about? I had never really thought about what that meant. I had gone from being master of my destiny, to being fearful of my investors, fearful of being honest, and fearful that actually I don't have the solution, and this could all be a house of cards crumbling around me.'

Three lunches. Three clients I thought I had helped to success. Three clients who wouldn't have done what they had done. So, where was I in making the world a better place? Where was I in helping them to achieve their dreams? They hadn't really thought about what their dreams were, either.

Maybe I had just picked the wrong three. I was sure there must be some successful and happy clients out there, who had done great deals because of me and my firm?

But all this made me realise just how important it was for me to work at my dreams. I did not want to carry on for another minute without knowing what they were.

Chapter 52: What's My Timeline? - John

It was initially awkward talking about myself without Rachel there, and also without Maria, but Neil explained what we would be doing. The first session would be about seeking things in the past which were positives to build on. The second session would be finding events and memories from the past which had been blocking me, things I needed to delete from my future. The third session would be about building my ideal future. He explained that this would be done using movement, and I thought that sounded very odd, but I had faith that he knew what he was doing, and just nodded.

We went through what Neil called the Timeline, and he gave me one of his rather ambiguous directions: If I could create a line anywhere on the floor to represent time, where would that line be? I chose a line which started at the settee and ended up by the large windows, leading out towards the fresh air. He then asked which end of the line was the past, and which end was the future. I said the future was the windows, and the beginning, by the settee, was the past. Then he asked me to go and stand on that line in the present moment, and I walked to where it felt right, which was just before halfway.

Then he asked me to close my eyes and walk back in time seeking moments where I felt specific things. The first thing he chose was love, and I was surprised when I stopped at a point where I felt love, about fifteen years ago in New York. I could see the views from our hotel room, near Times Square. I could see Rachel lying in bed and the sun coming through the windows, and its strange, misty glow on that early New York morning. Neil asked me where I was feeling that love, and it was in my heart and throughout my body. He asked me if it had a shape, and I said it felt like a huge red heart, glowing and beating, and that its red warmth was filling the rest of my body. He then asked me what I could hear. I could hear Rachel breathing gently, I could hear the faint noise of the cars down below, and I could hear the muted hum of the air conditioning. But most of all, I could hear Rachel breathing, a really lovely noise to hear. We did the same with smell, and taste, and then Neil gave me a card with 'love' written on it and I placed it on that spot.

We repeated the exercise with fulfilment, and I stopped at the time when I graduated, at the ceremony at Coventry Cathedral. I felt the limp handshake of the vice chancellor, and the paper scroll in my hand, my degree certificate, and looked at the big crowd and thought, *Yes, I've worked hard for this for three years, this is something I actually deserve, and I've had fun too.* I placed the 'fulfilment' card on this spot, twenty years ago.

I did the same for intimacy, although I wasn't sure what Neil really meant by this. But it took me back to just a few months ago, when I was lying in bed next to Rachel and felt really close to her. I wanted to make love, but we didn't need to, so we just lay there, holding each other with our eyes closed. I could feel her body moving against me, as she breathed in and out, and the warmth of her skin, and could smell the faint smell of her perfume. It was really strange having these waves of feeling, and being able to recall the details.

The last card was 'contentment'. Had I ever felt really content? But then I went back a few weeks to having dinner together, as a family, and us talking openly and honestly with each other. Even the kids were chatting. I could smell the food. I could hear the kids' voices and see the smiles on their faces. It was a magical moment, and maybe this was what fatherhood was all about, seeing these seeds of yours grow up to be something interesting and good? It felt like being filled with a rainbow...wow.

Then Neil got me to go right back to the beginning, when I was born, and walk along the line, stopping at each of those moments and engaging with each of them. Then again, more quickly; and then again without stopping. The final time he asked me to pick up the cards and engage with all those feelings, all those memories, in the present moment, holding the cards close to me. Half of me felt a bit weird, doing this; but part of it felt so real, especially when Neil asked me to think of something in the future, when I wanted to re-engage with the feelings. I thought about Rachel sailing across the Atlantic, and that I would be at home on my own with the kids. I threw the cards into that future, and took a deep breath and stepped forward a few weeks, picked them up, and held them close to me. I experienced a very strong sensation of all those different feelings merging together, making this delicious cocktail of sizes, shapes and colours, of goodness, of power, of the really important resources they were.

Then Neil asked me to 'anchor' those feelings, by choosing a card that had particular resonance and 'stepping' into the shape I had felt when I thought about it. I chose that moment of love in the hotel room in New York, and the warm glow of red grew and grew. When Neil asked me to score it out of ten, I said it was an eight. He asked me if I would like it to be even stronger, and I said, 'Yes, if that's possible.' He asked me to imagine that near my right hand was a control knob, marked from nought to ten, and that if I wanted I could reach out and turn that knob from eight to as high as I would like it to go. With my eyes closed, I reached out and turned that knob right up to ten. (If it had been a Marshall amp, it would have gone up to eleven!) When, as instructed, I stepped back into that hotel room I noticed things I hadn't noticed before: the clarity of the light on Rachel's skin, her body moving as she was breathing, the details of her hair and her eyelashes and lips. I felt a sense of love that I had never really noticed before, and I wanted to stay there, in that moment, forever.

Neil then explained that, with practice, I could be in that moment, with that sense of love, any time I wanted, consciously or subconsciously. I could move from a position of unhappiness to love. I promised I would practice this, because it was such an amazing place to be.

I booked a second session with Neil for a week later, which would be about going back into the past to seek things I might like to change to a disassociated perspective. This sounded a bit worrying. This first session had been incredibly powerful, and had taken me to places I had never, ever thought I could be... Did I really want to go back to some of the bad stuff?

When the second session started, I admit I wanted to end it immediately, and go back to somewhere good, but Neil encouraged me to think about things from the past which were blocking me, or causing unhelpful patterns of behaviour. The feelings that came up for me were being ridiculed, not valued, and feeling lonely and sad. We did a similar exercise, going back in time and seeking out those moments, like the boys laughing at me in the showers, and the Mini Willy experience. This was incredibly embarrassing for me, but I was determined to listen to Neil. He asked me to stand in those moments and have a conversation with the older John, the John who was here in the room now, which I was not comfortable with. I wasn't quite sure what I was supposed to say...

But then I saw myself as the John now, older and stronger, and I told the young John that actually there was nothing wrong with his body, it was just that he'd been growing at a different rate to the other boys. The fact they had ridiculed me was about them, I said, not me. I wondered, as the young John, what impact this had had on the older John, and we had a conversation about that too, and I realised I was the one holding him back by still being that young, lonely boy who felt ridiculed. But I wasn't that young John anymore. The older John acknowledged that, and thanked me for my words of wisdom, and he said he would try and leave that feeling in the past. As a person, physically and mentally, he was OK, and he didn't need to drag that stuff around with him like a rucksack full of sharp, heavy rocks. Back as me, in the room, the older John had a sense the rucksack was no longer there. It was parked somewhere back at that school.

We repeated the exercise as an even younger boy, with my father sending me off to boarding school, and not giving me praise for what I had achieved, and what I had worked hard for. I had a similar conversation with the younger John, but what also came up was who my father was, and where he had come from, and what he had been trying to achieve. I realised his words of criticism and his lack of praise was only what he had learnt from his parents, and that my father's intentions were actually good, he was just unable to express his emotions because he simply didn't have the vocabulary. I forgave my father, right then, for doing what he thought was best, even though it was actually the wrong thing for me. And I forgave my younger self for taking all that on board rather than just letting it wash off me. I felt like I had been cleansed; like a grey sludge had been washed out of my body about not being good enough, and not being valued. It hadn't all gone, but the space left behind could be filled with feeling good about myself.

I got back home, and Rachel was pleased to see me. The kids were too. Rachel asked how it had gone, and I told her it was tough but good. I told her I would like to talk about it more, but as it was part of a trilogy, could I finish first and then talk about it? She said, 'Of course.' And added that whenever I wanted to talk about it she would be ready to listen.

Session three was about my dreams. What was this going to bring up? We used the timeline exercise again, but this time going forward to my ideal future. I closed my eyes and walked forward about five years. I was asked where I was, and what I could see and hear and feel and smell and taste. I saw a bright, sunny morning, and I was lying on a big bed. I looked to my left and Rachel was there, still asleep and breathing gently. The house looked very familiar? And then I realised it was where we lived now, and that was a bit of a shock to me, because don't ideal futures involve being somewhere different? (Not on a yacht, for me, but maybe in a villa somewhere?)

When I went downstairs, there was the same familiarity, but I had a sense that there was no rush. I looked at the calendar and realised it was a Wednesday, and I looked for my briefcase, which was normally by the front door, but it wasn't there. I made some coffee and took it back upstairs, and a green tea for Rachel. Rachel stirred from her sleep, smiled and held her arms out. She told me to come back to bed for a while, so I did, and we made love.

After a relaxed breakfast with the kids, Rachel said she had to go because she had an important meeting. I started to think, *Where is this going?* and looked for some clues around me. I went into all the rooms and discovered one of the rooms was my office, but not my usual office. There were files, a computer, and a big whiteboard with names of clients written on, and I worked out I was doing a similar thing to now, just from home.

My focus, it appeared, was helping business owners achieve their dreams – their real dreams – using my legal skills with acquisitions, sales, mergers or whatever. That felt really good, and I was much more relaxed about doing it: no commute, no office hierarchy, just a few associates whose expertise I could access if I needed to.

After a day of work, bizarrely, Rowena and I went for a run when she got home from school. We did 5K, which was good practice because we were both booked to do a half marathon in six months' time.

Also bizarrely, I cooked the dinner for when Rachel got back home, and I really enjoyed cooking, making a contribution to the wellbeing of the family! James helped me, when he got home, and it was great. Jenny, too, was laughing. Rachel's meeting had gone well. She wasn't being paid enough for what she was doing, I thought, but she was happy and fulfilled.

After chatting in bed later, I went to sleep feeling really contented.

All of this came as a bit of a surprise to me! It was not the dream I imagined, but it felt very authentic and worth working towards. It was wonderful to see Rachel fulfilled, and to be cooking with James, and running with Rowena, and seeing Jenny with a happy smile on her face rather than a scowl.

Was this my future? We talked it through, in time chunks of various years, then months, then weeks and days, how I needed to get to there from here. I felt very excited. I had my plan!

When I got back home Rachel and I talked, a lot. She thought it was amazing that I had even discovered her future! I laughed and said maybe I shouldn't have given that secret away!

My future beckoned.

Chapter 53: Rachel's Future

Well, I had some first steps laid out, but I also wanted to keep things growing with John. It felt at times as if we were growing at different speeds, and maybe even in different directions. I didn't want that. I wanted him to grow faster, but he had his own pace and I couldn't force that.

I could still sense some anger from John about my sailing course, and that I was doing something without his having approved it in advance, but this was important to me. If I didn't take this step forward, I would stay stuck as I was.

I handed over the instructions to my parents, said goodbye to the kids, and to John, and reminded him I was only going to be away for a week. To his credit, he gave me a brave smile and a hug and wished me well, and off I went early on Monday morning to drive down to the Hamble.

I was really excited but nervous about the course. I had done the theory course online and had passed that. We started the day with health and safety stuff, and then a reminder of the basics of navigation to ensure we were all at an acceptable standard of passage planning and position finding. We were also taught the rudiments of boat handling.

That evening some of us got talking about our lives over dinner in a local pub. We were aged between twenty-five and sixty-five, with six men and two women, including me. The other woman, Jo, was about my age, and she told me her husband was a really keen sailor and she wanted to learn more so that she could sail more frequently with him, and share what he loved doing.

The next day we were kitted out in foul weather gear and life jackets, although the weather looked like it would stay fairly warm and sunny. We were split into two groups of four and allocated to two thirty-six-foot Beneteaus, and I was surprised by the space and, unlike a dinghy, the boat didn't move when I walked about. We were shown around the boats, where the life raft was, where we would attach life lines if it got really rough, where the engine was, and what to check in terms of its connections and condition. Then we cast off. The wind was blowing about force four from the west, and as we got out from the Hamble into the Solent, we could feel the boat heeling. Our destination was to head west towards the Needles. The spray was flying and it felt quite exciting. We took it in turns to take the helm. I wasn't used to steering a boat with a wheel, as the dinghies I sailed had tillers, and to begin with it felt quite difficult.

The days flew past. The camaraderie amongst the crew was great, and the sense of competition with the other boat made our journeys even more exciting. It was wonderful to share experiences over dinner, and feel we were all growing in knowledge together, increasing our capabilities and our confidence. I was the only one who was planning to sail the Atlantic, though, and people seemed almost in awe of that!

On the Thursday evening I met the couple who were planning on sailing across the Atlantic, Gavin and Jasmine, at a very famous pub and restaurant in Bursledon, called the Jolly Sailor. I was quite nervous. This was a big opportunity for me. Would they like me? Would I like them? Would I trust them enough to spend four weeks of my life doing something dangerous and difficult with them in charge? Gavin bought me a drink, and they told me a little about their life, which had been spent working hard building up their businesses, which they now ran together. They both loved sailing, but had quickly got tired of sailing round the Solent. After sailing down to the Mediterranean, they decided they wanted to sail across the Atlantic, to the Caribbean.

In a few weeks they were going to be heading out to Las Palmas in the Canaries, ready for the voyage across the Atlantic starting in November. Their eldest son, Rory, was going to go with them. He was twenty-five and a graduate, but had taken a gap year working as a sailing instructor while he worked out what career he wanted. Their daughter, Michelle, had been planning on going too, but she had just graduated as a nurse, and wasn't that keen on sailing, so hence the need for a fourth crew member.

I told them about my life, and the sailing I had done, and my dream to sail the Atlantic. They listened attentively, and I sensed they were in tune with me. We seemed to get on well, and Jasmine said it would be really helpful for us to spend a bit more time together. They also said they would like to meet John, because it was important to know he was behind me and I wasn't escaping from anything. I felt a little bit shocked at this, but I could see where they were coming from. They also said it might be good if, somehow, we could do some sailing together to find out how we got on with each other under canvas. We then talked about the practicalities of flights and the sharing of costs. I suggested that maybe one weekend we could charter a boat and go sailing. Gavin looked thoughtful, because this is a pretty expensive thing to do, but agreed we had to get to know how we worked together.

A couple of weeks later I got a phone call from Jasmine saying that a friend of theirs was going sailing round the Isle of Wight the next weekend, and was there any way I would be able to join them. I told John, and because he'd been following the plans he seemed OK with it.

It was good to see Gavin and Jasmine working together. There was almost a telepathy between them, and their confidence in each other's roles was great to see. We took it in turns changing roles, looking after the head sail, the main sail, the navigation, and the lookout, and I started to feel more useful and confident in my own abilities, especially as we sailed through the night, which I had never done before.

We arranged to meet up soon, so that they could talk to John, and I went back home really excited. The kids were delighted to see me; but my parents looked disapproving, and my mother said, 'Are you sure you know what you are doing?' I knew I had to talk to them about my big trip, and took the bull by the horns, explaining it would be winter when I went, so there wouldn't be much for Mum to do in the garden, and that some of the time the kids would be on school holidays, so they wouldn't have to worry about getting them up in the morning. I also suggested they meet Gavin and Jasmine, too, and have dinner with us all next Saturday evening. They agreed, and I felt like I'd made another step towards my dream.

The following week went by in a blur. Things with the kids were great, and John seemed relaxed too. Our relationship had gone from so much better, to rather tense, to a little easier.

When we all went out to dinner the next Saturday I was really relieved that John and Gavin seemed to get on OK. Jasmine and I talked with excitement about the voyage to come, and on the drive home John said he was starting to understand a little more about sailing, and that he felt I would be safe with Gavin and Jasmine. Even my parents seemed to like them, a little.

A couple of months later it was time to go. I had bought all the kit I needed, and had agreed where to meet Gavin and Jasmine in Las Palmas. I said long farewells to James, Jenny and Rowena, and even detected a few tears in James's eyes. Jenny was her usual self, not expressing emotions; but Rowena burst into tears and hugged and hugged me and said, 'Be safe, Mummy.' I burst into tears as well, and said I would send a postcard and see everybody in a few weeks. I waved goodbye, with my mother standing there looking disapproving, and headed off down the drive. John drove me to Gatwick, and after we had said our goodbyes he handed me a letter and said, 'Read this after you have started your trip, and have a wonderful journey. I will see you when you get back.' At that moment I admit I wondered if I could really leave these people, who I loved so much, and what impact it would have on them me being away. I almost wanted to turn around and say I'd changed my mind, but a huge part of me wanted to go ahead. I gave John a final kiss, and walked over to Departures, tears running down my cheeks.

Gavin and Jasmine's boat was called Eleuthera, which is Greek for freedom, and I found her on pontoon C, berth 42. *Wow*, I thought, as I looked at the forty-five-foot boat moored in the bustling Las Palmas marina, *this is really happening.*

The time just flew, as there was so much to do to get her ready. Then the day came for the off, the big start, with a hundred boats all crossing the starting line at around about the same time, none of us really racing but excited and keen to get going first. We held back, because we didn't want to get damaged in all the manoeuvring right at the start, and then we were off, heading west, land getting further and further away behind us, St Lucia a tiny dot on the map.

I admit I felt frightened as the land faded into the distance and the sun set. This would be the first time I had sailed out of sight of land, and there would be no going back, only 2,700 miles in front of us before we would see land again. *I have no choice*, I thought, *so I'd better just enjoy it.*

I suddenly remembered the letter that John had written me, and when I had a moment I went down to my bunk in the aft cabin and opened my kit bag. I found the envelope and, sitting down on my bunk, carefully opened it. Inside were several pieces of paper, a card and a photo. The pieces of paper were letters from each of the children. James wished me a good journey, and had unusually signed off with love and a kiss. Jenny expressed her love for me, which surprised me and brought tears to my eyes. Rowena had drawn a picture of me on a boat, smiling, with mermaids and dolphins all around me.

John's card was handwritten, and said to stay safe and have a wonderful journey, and that he couldn't wait to have me back in his arms to continue our journey. There was a red kiss for every year we had been together. The photo was of all four of them, as well as Woody, with a banner above them saying, 'We love you, Mum.'

The tears fell, and I wished I could reach out now and hug them; but instead I went back up on deck and faced northeast, a few thousand miles back to home, and opened my arms out to them.

Getting into a rhythm with three relative strangers, and having to keep watches of three hours on and nine hours off, with the time zones changing as we went west, was a challenge. But being on my own at night, just seeing the stars and the phosphorus and feeling the boat moving, was truly incredible, and I felt so free. There was a lovely, relaxed atmosphere on the boat, and when the sun went down below the yard arm we enjoyed the ritual of drinks – non-alcoholic – and food, and the opportunity to talk about anything and everything.

I felt more at peace than I had done for years, probably in my whole life, and particularly valued the time I had on my own, when the other three were sleeping or doing stuff down below.

We were really lucky with the weather. The trade winds came in early, and for much of the three weeks of our journey we were surfing down big waves. We saw dolphins, and flying fish at night, which sometimes landed on the boat, so we would eat them for breakfast. And there was this steady pattern of togetherness, all of us on one mission to land safely on the other side.

Excitement mounted as we got closer and closer to St Lucia. My navigation had been pretty good, and we got there twenty-one days later, having had an easy and really good voyage. It felt sad it was ending, but fantastic when we sailed into Marigot Bay, over the line, with hooters and a gun firing! We headed into the marina, where there were already many other competitors. What was really strange was that we hadn't seen any boats for most of the voyage. But then some had been heading further south, and others further north. We tied up in our berth and were welcomed by some of the organisers, who handed us rum punches, and the partying started – which they said would go on all night and the next night!

But there was a really big surprise waiting on the quay for me. John had flown in, and had the biggest smile on his face. He had been following my progress, and thought it would be lovely to be there to greet me. It was strange having John burst into my world like that, after so long apart, but it was also really good to see him there, and it felt like a huge step forward for him and for me.

A few days later, after a lovely time in St Lucia, the two of us flew back to England to start our new lives, again, and it felt so, so good.

*Everything that irritates us about others
can lead us to an understanding of ourselves.*

– Carl Jung

Chapter 54: Ups and Downs - Rachel

As everyone knows, you can sometimes look at people's lives from the outside and think they look very attractive, and maybe even wish you were like them because they are better looking, or have a nicer house, a bigger car, better teeth...and it made me wonder what people might think of us. The truth was, that all the stuff was just a façade, and what really mattered was the fact we were connected to each other for the first time in a long time and we could talk about pretty much anything. I also had a sense we were growing for the first time in years, both as individuals and as a couple.

Good things take work, and for too many years we had assumed life would go on, and our relationship would be OK, without paying it any attention. That was a huge mistake because a great relationship, as we learnt, takes a huge investment of time and energy, and requires a lot of openness, honesty, vulnerability and trust. We were really fortunate that chance had taken us to the place where we met Richard and Olivia, who gave us the key to understanding ourselves and our relationship: Neil and Maria.

Sailing the Atlantic had opened up my thinking about all sorts of possibilities and, eventually, when the time was right, it led me to a different career. I was now using the marketing skills I had learnt all those years ago at university helping a really worthwhile charity, the Brain Tumour Charity, and organising funding for research into finding a cure for this awful disease. The hours were long, and the money not great, but we were measuring little successes as we went along in the hope that all this work would come up with good results. It felt important, and I finally felt the fulfilment I had been longing for.

Life at home was not a bed of roses – and to hope that it would be was dreadfully unrealistic. John was pursuing his own path of finding out what he really wanted, and that was difficult and frustrating for me to watch sometimes, but at times I was able to help him.

The children were great, most of the time. As with any child and teenager's lives, it was a bit up and down, but we worked hard to help them understand what they wanted out of life and to have a really good relationship with them.

Sadly, one day, Woody died, at the age of thirteen, and that was awful. I had been so close to him. He had been my soulmate for years. It was heart-breaking to hold him as he faded away, but I gave him permission to go, and as the sun started to rise in the sky he gave one last shudder and died in my arms. I cried like I had never cried before, holding his body, feeling his warmth slowly ebb away.

I started thinking about getting another puppy; not to take his place, but to fill our lives with fur and joy. I talked to John about it, as he'd never been keen on dogs, but he understood my needs, and soon Willow became a part of our lives.

In terms of John and I, as I said, life wasn't a bed of roses, and we had to keep reminding ourselves that this wouldn't happen magically, or automatically, we needed to carry on working at it. We agreed we would go back and see Neil and Maria for annual check-ups, to remind ourselves of the important techniques to use, as well as giving ourselves some new tools, as appropriate. That became a lovely routine, and helped us deal with things we felt were going wrong.

Of course there were times when John really irritated me, and I must have irritated him, but at least we were able to talk about it now. It was interesting that John's perception seemed to change in time, and he seemed to get less irritated with the little things and let them pass him by. That relieved a lot of the potential conflict.

We had lots of discussions about schooling for the children.

John had been very keen that James and Jenny went to his old school, West Dene; but when we talked more about it, we agreed that actually this wasn't the best thing for them, so all three of them ended up going to the local state school. Some things about the school were good, and some of it wasn't so good, but it was much more real than being shut away in a boarding school with a bunch of overprivileged kids inflated by an unjustified sense of entitlement. All three of the children made friends with good kids, which was great, because they were learning to make their own decisions about the people they wanted to be with.

All three of them seemed remarkably mature for their ages, and able to deal with life. I hoped that the example we had given them in coming back from the brink, and showing love and support for each other, and them, was helpful in them learning to cope with life. That made me feel quite proud.

I was so grateful this was the direction we were moving in, one I hadn't expected. And I was happy I hadn't run away, hoping the grass would be greener on the other side. We had found ways of sorting out our problems, and we were both working together to keep that going.

Chapter 55: Ups and Downs - John

The foundations for my future seemed much firmer than they had a while ago, and it felt great to be in love with Rachel again – although in love in a different way, in a much more realistic and positive way. I felt empowered by having more control over my life, to be aiming for what was important to me, rather than just following a path somebody else had laid out for me.

In terms of my work life, I started to get much greater clarity. I would continue doing what I had trained to do, as I was actually good at it, and I could find it fulfilling; but I decided fighting my way up the equity partnership ladder, and the daily grind of commuting into London, was really stressful, and I needed to find a different and better way of working.

A chance conversation with an ex-colleague over lunch, one day, set me in a new direction. His name was Jamie and he worked in a large firm and we had come across each other, sometimes on opposing sides of the table, but he had set up his own corporate finance boutique specialising in helping smaller businesses acquire new companies, dispose of companies or acquire funding. When he described the sort of work he was doing I felt quite jealous, because he worked from home, he could pick and choose his clients, and take time out when he needed it. But he also had the excitement of doing some interesting deals.

When he told me that the work coming in was more than he could cope with on his own, my breath stopped, and when he looked at me and said, 'I wonder if you would be interested in working with me?' something clicked, and I said yes immediately, I would love to explore that idea.

Over the next couple of weeks we had various meetings, talking about the realities of how it would work. He lived in Guilford, not a million miles from me in East Horsley, and what we decided was that if we were going to work together and grow, we would need our own separate office, somewhere clients could come for meetings, and where we could have some support staff.

I talked to Rachel about this and laid out the plans and the possibilities, and she was excited but a bit worried about the impact it would have on earnings. I described how it would be a fairly smooth transition, because there was already a workflow there, so I wouldn't be starting with a clean sheet of paper. I had some clients who might want to transfer once I had got through my restrictive covenants. I also had good contacts with banks, VCs, accountants and corporate finance houses who, I was sure, would pass work my way. Although I would be earning much less to begin with, I was sure our client base would grow. It was lovely that Rachel could hear the excitement in my voice, and that I felt this was going to lead me to a better place, and she agreed. She asked me what she could do to help, and I laughed and said, 'Spending less money would be good.' Then I said, 'No, that's not fair, it will be OK, I'm sure it will be.'

Jamie and I agreed a start date, and I spoke to my senior partner and explained what I was doing. He was really shocked and said, 'John, we had you marked out as one who was going to grow with the firm long term, and have a great future.' I explained I had changed, that my priorities had changed, and he thought hard about it and then said, 'In a way I almost envy you, and I hope it will work out well for you. I have got to say, though, you know what the rules are on poaching clients are, don't you?...' I assured him I did. And then he asked me if I would be prepared to work as a consultant for the company if the workload was such that they needed to call on me. I said I would.

We agreed a three-month transition period to hand over clients, and my wind down started. It was strange to be focusing on leaving a firm I had been with since qualifying, to be leaving a group of people who'd been there, every day, in the office and on the train to and fro to Waterloo, but who I hardly knew. We'd barely spoken. What a world.

The last day of work arrived, and we had a lunchtime drinks party, where the senior partner made a speech, and I left carrying a few bags of personal stuff and, wow, it felt really strange. There was no gold clock, no engraved certificate; but I left with the knowledge I could go back, and a handshake from those who respected me – and also said they envied me.

We found a small suite of offices in Guilford town centre. The rent was high, but the location was good and work started. The clients were a bit smaller, and it was great to be able to dig deeper into why they were doing what they were doing, and to tailor our services to meet their needs.

Life got into a new rhythm; a later start, an earlier finish. Life at home was still good, but as time went by the ups and downs changed. The ups became more up, with Rachel regularly reminding me that the fun part still needed to be worked on. The intimacy became less frequent, but the emphasis was on quality and that was OK. The children got older, and we decided they would go to the local school rather than going away to public school, which saved money and meant we could be there for them during the difficult teenage years. My parents were upset, because they were going to pay anyway; but part of me felt that no, I didn't want them to be brought up amongst the privileged few, with an air of entitlement. The local schools were pretty good, and I thought it would be beneficial for them to mix with real people rather than learn in a protected environment. I'd found I actually wanted to be with them, anyway, which was a significant shift for me, and one which made me very happy. They found it a bit of a struggle at first, but made good friends; and the teachers seemed to be doing an OK job in difficult circumstances.

What I did notice was the big impact that little things can have, and how easy it was to get things out of context. For instance, when I got back home and saw dirty washing and dirty dishes I'd still get upset about them; but after a time I began to wonder what I was gaining by getting upset about these little things? Before, I would store them away, building up resentment, and then one day explode and shout and get angry, attaching meaning to this small stuff, which was wrong. Rachel hadn't not loaded the dishwasher because she didn't love me... That was one of the interesting connections I made, and I learnt to filter these things out because they weren't important, and I started to look for the good things which were happening rather than the bad things.

We had got out of the habit of having our Daily Blessings chat every night, and our State of the Union meetings. One evening, during one of my stored-up, festering blowouts, I stopped myself mid-rant and thought, John, this is crazy, and I explained to Rachel how I was feeling, and the two of us had a very open discussion. We shared the things that caused irritation and it felt really great to clear the air.

We then talked like two adults about what we needed to do differently, how to explain how we were feeling about certain things, and to make it easier to open the door to expressing those feelings. We agreed a code word: 'porcupine'. The purpose of that code word was to signal that something was happening for one of us, like, 'I'm getting out of control' or 'I'm getting upset or angry and I really need to talk about it'. I'm not ashamed to admit that 'porcupine' got used occasionally, and it enabled us to talk and share our feelings and laugh, and then move on. It was a great way of connecting and getting those little things to dissipate. Now when the butterfly flaps its wings on the other side of the world, we can talk about it rather than it building up into a hurricane!

A phrase I had remembered from our counselling really resonated, and that was, 'Freedom is the ability to pause between stimulus and response.' No longer did I need to jump straight in and react. I gave myself the time to think about what had happened, the impact it was having on me, and, most importantly, the impact I wanted it to have on me, and then I could give the right response. That felt really empowering.

Yes, life certainly had its ups and downs, but wow, it was absolutely moving in the right direction.

Epilogue 1: John

Ten years on. Life had changed a huge amount.

The children were all grown up, pretty much. James had been to university and was on the first rung of the career ladder. He was living in London and had had a few girlfriends. He seemed OK living a busy life, driving around the country looking after a chain of retail stores. Jenny, too, had been to university. She followed her love of sport and became a PE teacher at a comprehensive school in Nottingham. She loved her work, and was baking lots of cakes in her spare time. Rowena was in her first year studying art at Loughborough. She was occupying a very different world, and was finding herself, and I was concerned about some of the things happening in her life. She'd never really had any boyfriends, and seemed to find relationships difficult; but we had a great relationship, and I made time to go and see her up in Loughborough.

Rachel had done her one trans-Atlantic trip and she wanted to do more. She loved sailing, and even managed to get me out on a boat a couple of times. The first time it was calm with not much wind, and the boat hardly moved and that was OK. The next time it was rough and windy, and I felt a bit seasick and decided this definitely wasn't for me, but I encouraged her to enjoy it!

We were doing more things together, and had got through several things on our bucket list. We had to remind ourselves not to drift, and to keep focused on communication, connection, commitment, fun and growth, and we decided it would be good to go and see Neil and Maria for annual MOTs. This was great, and made us check in with each other and our physical and mental wellbeing. (I'm not allowed to use the words 'OK' or 'nice' anymore.

I have to use other, more descriptive words to explain how I'm feeling, which is good!)

Rachel has her new career, working for the Brain Tumour Charity as head of marketing, and using the skills she learnt selling soap to the masses. The hours are long, and the work is difficult for her sometimes, but she's working with a great team of people and gets real fulfilment. Her passion and energy for raising money for research might hopefully one day pay off.

The fact that the kitchen still sometimes looks like a bombsite was less important than it used to be, and we found we could spend time doing the important things and having fun together. We take it in turns to choose, and that is a rhythm we manage to keep up, regardless of other stuff going on.

My work wasn't straightforward, as working with another person with different thoughts could be quite a battle at times, but at most other times we worked well as a team. Our business grew, and we took on a couple of newly qualified lawyers to take some of the grunt work out of it. We became known as a firm which could offer good, pragmatic advice, and I learnt that saying no was OK if we were feeling overloaded. I looked forward to work, and most days I left feeling I had used my skills in law to positive effect. Although the money I was earning was less, that wasn't important.

We had kept in touch with Richard and Olivia – well, Rachel had more than me – and we'd met up a few times and shared stories. They said they felt really 'privileged' to have met us, and were so happy we had contacted Neil and Maria.

I asked Rachel if she fancied going back to the same place, in Grenada, for our tenth anniversary, to see who we could pass that knowledge on to, and she laughed.

We decided we would. It was a momentous event in some ways, and quite natural in others to want to go back to the beginning of when things started to change for us. We booked a ten-day trip, and this time we managed to get a free upgrade to Upper Class on Virgin going out and coming back! I was looking forward to seeing whether the place had changed at all, and, when we arrived, the sun was still the same, the airport terminal was a bit bigger and a bit less chaotic, but the look and smell of the place was much as I remembered. We had a slightly bigger room overlooking the sea, which was great.

Rachel went sailing, of course. And I enjoyed some beach volleyball. But we did stuff together too, walking hand in hand along the beach, swimming together, playing together and going on trips around the island.

One evening, as we were having a meal, Rachel said, 'Look around you, pick out the couples who are getting on well and those who might be struggling.'

As I studied the couples around us I said to Rachel, 'I wonder what would happen if we saw a couple, like Richard and Olivia did with us, who are struggling, and we opened up a conversation? What would that be like?'

Rachel said, 'I think you call that an opportunity to pay it forward.'

The next night, when I was standing at the bar, I noticed a couple next to me. There was something about the communication between them which seemed quite strained. They didn't seem happy, and after a few moments the wife went off to the ladies' room.

Rachel came up to me and whispered, 'I think they are the ones,' and went to find a table.

I introduced myself to Tom, and we got talking. He was there with his wife Sarah, and I found it unreal that I was able to ask him questions which allowed him to open up; he just started off loading on me about how they'd been married for fifteen years and had come here to decide whether to stay together or split up – was there something about this place? They had two children, who they obviously loved, but who caused stress. Tom was an accountant who hated his job, but he was on the treadmill, trying to become a partner, commuting every day to London from Winchester. I couldn't believe it. So many things Tom said made me want to laugh and say, 'That was me!'

I felt prickles running down the back of my neck and my spine and later I said to Rachel, 'This is unreal; this is history repeating itself. How do you feel about this?'

Rachel said, 'I'm really excited, and I think we may be able to help them in the same way as Richard and Olivia helped us!'

And so it was that the power of what we had learnt was extended.

I looked at Rachel, at the lines around her eyes, the body that had given birth to our three children, and I felt a deep gratitude for her, for everything we were now, and everything we would yet be, and for the ultimatum she gave me, ten years ago, that had changed our lives.

Epilogue 2: Rachel

John, for once, reminded me our anniversary was coming up – our ten-year anniversary, though? – and when I looked puzzled he said that on this date ten years ago we had flown out to Grenada. John suggested it would be great to mark that significant moment in our lives by going back to Grenada, to the same place, but I was a bit reluctant. I was concerned it would be a disappointment, or might trigger some of the more unpleasant memories of that time, but John was really keen, so I agreed.

This time, I spoke to the check-in girl and explained this was a very special anniversary for us, and she tapped away on the computer and gave a big smile and said, 'We would love to upgrade you.' My heart leapt! We felt like two kids who had been given the keys to a sweet shop! It was so lovely to turn left on the plane, and be shown to our properly reclining seats. I looked through the giveaway bag of toiletries, and the pyjamas – wow! We drank champagne, ate a delicious meal, watched some movies, slept, and landed in Grenada.

We were greeted by the same amazing smell of the air, the sea and the flowers, and as we went in through the gates I was reminded of just how much our lives had changed because of the chance encounter with Olivia and Richard.

John was a very different person this time; much more sociable and happy, and I was curious to see him listening empathically to a man at the bar. He then introduced me to Tom and to Sarah, his wife, and when the men went off to talk she started to open up, quite naturally, about her feelings and what their life had become. It was like I was sitting in the place of Olivia, ten years ago; but now

I had the chance to help an unhappy couple get somewhere better. We had dinner, the four of us, just like we had with Richard and Olivia, and I felt such a warmth at the thought of having sprinkled a little magic, like they had. We parted good friends, with the promise we would stay in touch.

Life went on, and it was good, most of the time. What was great was that the downs were generally about outside influences, things that neither of us had any control over. I noticed that John had become strangely philosophical. He wasn't at a place where he would come meditating with me, or to yoga, but was much more able to deal with life.

Our closeness was a calm and contented place; our love-making passionate, and occasionally surprising – although not frequent enough for John. We tried to maintain our routine of mentioning three good things every night, and our State of the Union meetings; but there were many times when we forgot, or got tied up in other things, especially with three teenage children, but we acknowledge the importance of doing it as often as we can.

I felt so lucky to still be with John, still communicating and connecting with each other regularly. I felt fulfilled in my job, and valued. And the kids were growing up to be very different, very amazing people, learning about life's ups and downs for themselves. I hoped we were good role models for them, because we had fought to make our relationship a better place. When I look at John now, as my husband, and their dad, I feel proud of him, and of us.

Epilogue 3: The Children

James

It was weird seeing Mum and Dad change when I was younger, and embarrassing when Mum kept talking to us about their therapy, but I really admire them too. So many couples just split up when they have problems – and now I've had a few girlfriends I can see how that happens – but they were so determined to talk through their problems instead, and work them out. I really am glad they didn't split up. That would have been awful.

Dad was so much more chilled in the end. He even cooked! I sometimes helped him, which was great, and Mum really appreciated having some food ready when she got home from work. It was great that she started work again. She seemed so much happier.

I hope when I get married one day I remember how hard they worked to stay together. Life at home was pretty good when they sorted their problems out, and started talking instead of yelling.

Jennifer

Mum used to drive me mad. Dad not so much. But then he was never there. She was so much happier when she started working, which was great. I remember when I got pretty stressed about my GCSEs, and Dad was amazing, really calm and helpful. I don't think he would have listened before.

I don't really know what went on in their counselling, but they stopped arguing all the time, and we really started to have some fun as a family, which was great. I'll never forget when I made him that chocolate cake and he looked so emotional, and Mum looked so happy somehow. And it was so funny when they decided they wanted to bake some cakes together, and I helped them. We got into a food fight, which was so funny. I never thought I'd see them laugh like that! Rowena looked pretty shocked, though!

Life is better now, for them. I'm glad they did the counselling. It saved our family from splitting up, like so many of my friends' families. That's so hard on the kids.

Rowena

I was pretty young when Mum and Dad started their therapy thing. I didn't really know what was going on. Mum stopped looking so sad, though. And Dad started talking to me about stuff. I liked that.

I thought they were going to have one of their arguments when Woody died, because Dad really didn't want another dog; but he really listened to Mum, and they got Willow, who is really sweet.

I'm not really into dating, and sometimes I really don't know what I want to do with my life, but I hope if I do meet someone I can have fun like Mum and Dad do now.

"When you find the person you love, an act of ancient recognition brings you together. It is as if millions of years before the silence of nature broke, his or her clay and your clay lay side by side. Then, in the turning of the seasons, your one clay divided and separated.

While your clay selves wandered for thousands of years through the universe, your longing for each other never faded.

It could be a meeting on the street, or at a party, or over a simple cup of coffee, then, suddenly there is the flash of recognition and the embers of kinship glow. There is an awakening between you, a sense of ancient knowing.

Love opens the door of ancient recognition. You enter. You come home to each other at last."

– an extract from John O'Donohue's
Anam Cara: Spiritual Wisdom from the Celtic World

Is your Relationship in stormy waters?
Visit **www.RelationshipParadigm.com** for guidance.

Are you ready to Retune your relationship?
Join us on an intensive group retreat in a beautiful part of England.
Go to www.RelationshipParadigm.com for more information.